Wind Loading Handbook

3279948 BK G WKD
MAIN LID

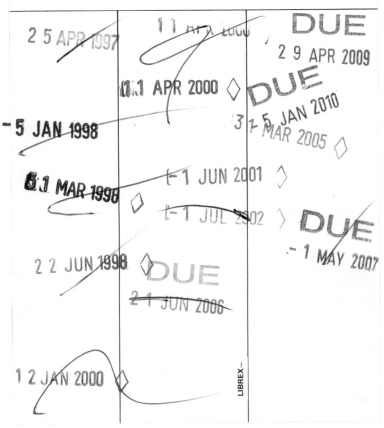

Wind Loading Handbook

Wind Loading Handbook

Guide to the use of
BS 6399 Part 2

T.V. Lawson F. Eng.

with an Article by M.J. Prior of the Meteorological Office

Butterworth-Heinemann
Linacre House, Jordan Hill, Oxford OX2 8DP
A division of Reed Educational & Professional Publishing Ltd

 A member of the Reed Elsevier plc group

OXFORD   LONDON   BOSTON
NEW DELHI   SINGAPORE   SYDNEY
TOKYO   TORONTO   WELLINGTON

First published 1996

© Reed Educational & Professional Publishing Ltd 1996

British Library Cataloguing in Publication Data
Lawson, T. V.
    Wind Loading Handbook: guide to the Use
    of BS 6399 Part 2
    I. Title
    624.175

ISBN 0 7506 1094 8

D
624.175
LAW ℮

Library of Congress Cataloguing in Publication Data
Lawson, T. V.
    Wind loading handbook: guide to the use of BS 6399 part 2 / by
    T. V. Lawson: with an article by M. J. Prior.
    p.   cm.
    Includes bibliographical references.
    ISBN 0 7506 1094 8
    1. Wind-pressure. 2. Building–Standards–Great Britain.
    I. Title.
    TH891.L33   95–37496
    624.1'75'021841–dc20   CIP

Printed and bound in Great Britain by
Hartnolls Limited, Bodmin, Cornwall

Contents

Introduction

The new Code of Practice for Wind Loads (BS 6399) Part 2 is much larger and more comprehensive than the Code it replaces; this is for three reasons:

(i) It gives quantitative criteria on whether the response of a structure is dynamic or not, and thus whether the wind loading on it is covered by the Code.

(ii) It covers a great many situations not covered in the last Code, CP3 Chapter V Part II, referred to throughout this Handbook as CP3.

(iii) The science of wind engineering has progressed a long way since CP3 was written and the data contained in the new Code are considered to be more accurate and extensive than those in CP3. With greater understanding the scope is enlarged, and, whilst the Code has been written to gain all the advantages of the new work, more complex calculations have to be made.

The members of the committee responsible for this Code were greatly concerned as to how this vast amount of new knowledge could best be made available in Code form. They were assisted in reaching their eventual conclusion by the advent of the universal use of computers, which make repeated computations simple. The decision was taken to include as much as is feasible for use in everyday calculations. However, it was decided to make the Code as similar to CP3 as possible; to this end two methods of calculation have been devised. In Section 2 of the Code a 'Standard' method is presented which is similar in form to, but more extensive than, CP3, but which, because of the simplifications, tends to give conservative results. A second method of calculation, called the 'Directional' method is presented in Section 3. Calculations using the Directional method are much longer but should provide smaller and more accurate estimates of the loading on the building.

The calculation of wind loads has four parts:

(i) The determination of whether the structure responds in a static or dynamic manner to the loading. The subject of the response of structures is considered at length in Article 3 of Chapter 4 of this Handbook. To summarize that article, a dynamic structure has the ability to store energy from one cycle of oscillation to the next, so that the energy causing the deformation, and therefore the internal stresses, is no longer directly related to the loads applied by the wind but is related to the amount of energy stored in the structure from previous loadings.

(ii) The determination of a value of Effective Wind Speed. In practice several values have to be calculated.

(iii) The determination of a set of Values of Pressure Coefficient related to the shape of the building.

(iv) The integration of the pressures over the surfaces of the building to obtain maximum loading over the whole or parts of the building.

The purpose of this Handbook is to assist the user of the Code in performing his task. It has four Chapters:

- Chapter 1 consists of two halves: in the first the steps to be taken by someone using the Code infrequently to arrive at a design load are described. The second half consists of a description of the steps, in the form of computer programs, which the author considers would be useful for someone who expects to use the Code on many occasions. This chapter has been placed at the front of the Handbook for ease of access as it is probably the chapter to which reference will be made most often. In explaining parts, especially certain choices of method to be made, the reader will be referred forward to some of the examples in Chapter 3. By careful choice of the examples, the reader can see the circumstances in which it is advantageous to use one method or the other, and can also see the additional amount of work to be carried out to achieve that gain.

- In Chapter 2 the reader is taken through the Code paragraph by paragraph, amplifying or explaining as required so that the intention of the Code is fully understood. It also contains a detailed index so that specific items in the Code can be located quickly.

- Chapter 3 consists of a series of worked examples, which can be used to calibrate any computer programs written by the user for his own use. There are separate examples in the calculation of wind speeds and loads.

- Chapter 4 consists of a series of articles each on a separate underlying aspect of wind engineering which together form the basis of this Code. These articles are in the form of background presentations of the fundamentals of the subject and are not required for the correct and effective application of the Code.

Acknowledgements

Extracts from BS 6399: Part 2: 1995 are reproduced with the permission of the British Standards Institute (BSI). Users of this Handbook are reminded that calculations should only be carried out using the Code. Complete copies of the Code can be obtained by post from BSI Customer Services, 389 Chiswick High Road, London W4 4AL. Telephone 0181 996 7000.

BS 6399 was assembled by an Original Drafting Group (CSB/54/2) to the stage when the document went out for Public Comment. On the receipt of comments, the Code was produced in its final form by a Finalisation Group; the members of both groups are listed below. The final document was then submitted to the Main Committee for approval.

At meetings of the Original Drafting Group it was considered desirable that a Handbook should be produced simultaneously with the Code, a Handbook whose purpose was to supply back-up information on the thoughts behind the Code to prevent it turning into a text book, and also to supply guidance in its application. Throughout the drafting process items were included in the Code with the comment that an explanation should be included in the Handbook.

The membership of the Groups are as follows:

Original Drafting Group	*Finalisation Group*
B.H. Fisher (Chairman) deceased	R.S. Narayanan (Chairman)
R.S. Narayanan (Chairman)	A. Allsop
P.Beckmann	Prof N. Cook
Prof N. Cook	T.V. Lawson
H. Gulvanessian	Dr A.P. Robertson
R.I. Harris	B.W. Smith
T.V. Lawson	N. Tutt
M.J. Prior	
B.W. Smith	
N. Thompson	
R.E. Whitbread	
G.W. Wiskin	
Dr T.A. Wyatt	

Dr W.W.L. Chan was *ex-officio* member of both groups in his capacity as Chairman of B/525/1 and previously CSB/54. His participation in the work of the Groups is appreciated.

All members of both Groups have had an input to this Handbook and this is gratefully acknowledged; however Professor Nick Cook and Brian Smith have made invaluable suggestions at all stages of the preparation of the Handbook, have read drafts and offered detail suggestions for additions and suggested some rewording of paragraphs and sentences. Without their input the Handbook would be a very much poorer document.

1
The steps to be taken in the use of the Code

Steps useful for infrequent users

Step 1 Determination of the dynamic sensitivity of the building (See Paragraph 1.6 and Annex C)[1]

If the natural frequencies and structural damping of the building are known, then the product of K_h and K_b could be calculated from equation 5 in Annex C of the Code and the value of C_r from equation 3. These equations require the knowledge of the Basic Wind Speed, the 'fetch' and 'topography' factors and the 'terrain correction factor' (see C.2.1. in Annex C), which, at this stage are often unknown. It is recommended here that K_b and K_h are calculated from equations 9 and 10.

If the natural frequencies and structural damping of the building are not known, or a quick estimate is required, then a building-type factor can be obtained from Table 1, and, with this, and the height of the building, the value of C_r can be obtained from Figure 3.

If the value of C_r is less than 0.25 and the height of the building is less than 300 m, then the procedures of the Code apply, and the value of C_r should be stored for future use.

If the value of C_r is greater than 0.25, or the height of the building is greater than 300 m, then the Code does not apply and a full dynamic study must be undertaken. *However the data in this Code are suitable for the calculation of Cladding loads because the maximum loads in panels are imparted by the wind at every cycle, and the panel does not store energy. A value of 0.0 for C_r is used for all Cladding.*

Step 2 The pick-and-mix principle

Next choose the more appropriate of Standard or Directional method for the calculation of wind speeds and pressure coefficient separately. Guidance is given in the following two sections and then there is another Pick-and-Mix section.

---

[1] In this Handbook, paragraph numbers in boxes at the start of headings refer to paragraphs in the Code of Practice for Wind Loads (BS 6399) Part 2.

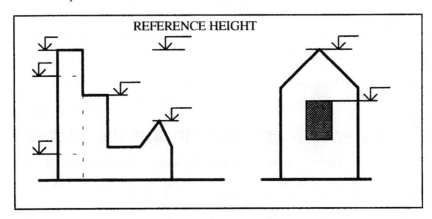

Diagram 1.1

Step 3　Choice of method for wind speed calculation

The wind speed used for design purposes is called the Effective Wind Speed calculated for the Effective Height of the building. If the height of the building is greater than 100 m, then the Directional method must be used (see Section 1.5.1. Stage 6). In many instances a value or values will be needed at several effective heights: this may occur because the 'division by parts' rule is applied or because the 'Reference Height' for different components of the building is different. For this reason the time involved in the calculation may be a factor in the choice of method.

If the Standard Method is to be used to evaluate the values of Pressure Coefficient, then it is recommended that only the maximum value of wind speed for all wind directions is calculated. This can be achieved by using a

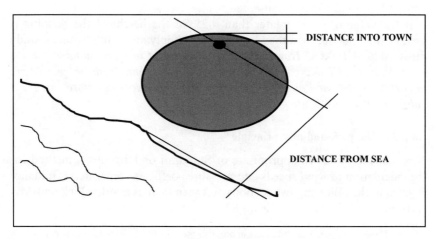

Diagram 1.2

Direction Factor of 1.0 and using the nearest distance from the sea and the shortest distance from the edge of the town, if the building is located within one.

The effect of the area over which maximum correlation of load is required is quantified by the diagonal 'a', and is illustrated in Figure 5. This is always associated with a face or 'combined faces' and does not vary with wind direction. In the Directional method it is taken into account using the 'Gust Factor' (g_t). The value of g_t is determined by the integration of the spectrum of turbulence from a zero frequency to a value dependent upon 'a'. Thus the value takes account of the actual turbulence present. To provide a simple approach, wherein the wind load on a panel of a different size can be determined by a single multiplication from the wind load on the original panel, a size factor applicable at the 'calculation of load' stage has to be devised. This is done in the Standard method: in the derivation of the 'Size Factor, C_a', three different values of turbulence have been assumed, corresponding to ranges of height and distances from the sea and into towns. The evaluation of C_a for the appropriate panel size, the diagonal 'a', is obtained from one of three curves, called A, B and C in Figure 4. A table, inset in Figure 4, informs which curve should be used. The use of C_a therefore includes an approximation about the turbulence which is treated differently in the Directional method.

Measurements of wind speeds over hills show that the shape of a hill affects the mean wind speed of the wind blowing over it, without affecting the fluctuating component. It can therefore be allowed for *correctly* only in the Directional method because, in that method, the mean and fluctuating components of wind speed are treated separately (by suffices c and t respectively of S and T). In the Standard method both components are contained in the single S_b factor. When the topography is considered in the Standard method an assumption has to be made about the intensity of turbulence, and a single conservative value is used for all instances. The assumption for turbulence in the Standard method is the same as in CP3.

In this *Handbook*, a direct comparison of the magnitude of wind speeds calculated by the two methods is only possible if the size correction factor for the Standard method (C_a) is introduced in the calculation of the wind speeds. This is done in the tables on pp. 74–97 of this Handbook. In order to show the advantages of using wind speeds calculated by the Directional method (usually lower values of wind speed, but involving more work), tables for similar situations are presented in Chapter 3 Group 1 Section 1. On pp. 74–82 are presented 'omnidirectional' values (values for which the directional factor has not been used) for building heights of 5 m, 20 m and 100 m. Separate tables are presented, for distances from the sea of 100, 50, 20, 10, 5 and 2 km and for each a range of distances into town. Different diagonal sizes are presented, the terminology is explained on p. 73. The values of R- - -, the ratio of the value for the Directional method divided by the value for the Standard method, give a direct comparison between the values derived from the two methods.

It must be remembered that the pressures vary as the square of the wind speed, so that a comparison of loads would vary as the square of R- - -.

It can be seen (on p. 81 for instance) that for Effective Heights of 100 m the Standard method gives slightly lower values (the ratio of the wind speed calculated by the Standard method divided by the wind speed calculated by the Directional method is down to 0.98) than the Directional method. For buildings above this height the remarks in Section 1.5.1 Stage 6 suggest that only the Directional method should be used. It would appear that the largest ratio of Wind Speeds for the two methods (Standard divided by Directional) is 1.20 (44 per cent increase in load), for an Effective Height of 5 m, falling to about 1.11 (23 per cent increase in load) for an Effective Height of 20 m. The larger gains are for the larger panel sizes. Readers can quickly see what gain is possible by looking for their situation, or as near as possible to their situation, on pp. 74–82.

So much for a comparison of the magnitude of the wind speed. A word is required about the work involved. In the Standard method a single value of wind speed is calculated for every Effective Height (or 12 if wind direction is considered). In the Directional method a different value of wind speed has to be calculated for every part with a different value of diagonal 'a'. The minimum number of calculations this will involve is three (panel, internal and face): if the wall and roof faces are of different sizes, then a different value should be calculated for each face. The calculations of different wind speeds based on different values of the diagonal 'a' for the various wall and roof faces can add up to a great many evaluations of wind speed, but is required by Section 3.2.3.3. It is considered in this Handbook that this is excessive for hand calculations and would recommend that the concept behind the permission in Section 3.2.3.3.3 for Cladding loads (to use the size factor (C_a) from the Standard method for the calculation of loads on panels of different sizes) be applied also to whole faces, based on the value for the smallest face. The smallest face would be called the Minimal Face. *This procedure would require that only three values of wind speed be calculated; for panel, internal volume and the minimal face.* The value of wind speed for other sizes of face and for 'combined faces' would be obtained by 'correcting' the loads on those faces by the ratio of the value of C_a for the face to its value for the Minimal Face; this would be done at the load calculation stage. This procedure is called option (v) in the Pick-and-Mix section below. At this stage the work involved in calculating three values of wind speed for 12 wind directions for every height should be considered in making the choice if option (v) is chosen.

Step 4   Choice of method for pressure coefficient calculation

The Standard method only gives values for pressure on walls and roofs for rectangular and circular buildings. It is suggested in Section 2.4.2 that polygonal buildings can be studied, but the reader is immediately referred to Sections 3.3.1.2 and 3.4.1 in the Directional method, and it is recommended

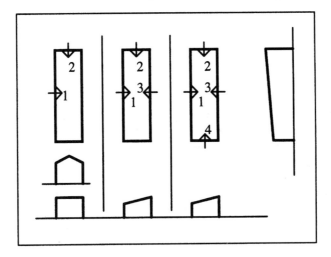

Diagram 1.3

in this Handbook that the Directional method is used in its entirety for these buildings.

The main difference between the methods is that, in the Standard method, only two cases are studied for buildings with flat, or equally duopitch or hipped roofs: the wind normal to the faces of the rectangle are studied in turn. The text explains that if the building is singly-symmetric or asymmetric then 3 or 4 cases have to be studied; this can only arise on a rectangular building if it has a non-flat roof. If the asymmetry arises because of a polygonal planform, then, the pressure coefficient data have to be obtained from the Directional method, and it is recommended in the last paragraph of this Handbook that the Directional method should be used in that case.

Thus, if the building is doubly symmetric and its orientation with respect to north is unknown, then the Standard method gives only slighter higher loads for much less work and should be used. If, however, the orientation is known, and either the larger sides face into the weakest winds (remember that the wind onto *both* of the longer faces has to be considered) or the roof is asymmetric, then there are possible reductions of load available[2] in using the Directional factors at the expense of extra work. But if the planform is

---

[2] Remember that, because ranges of wind direction of $\pm 45°$ and $(180° \pm 45°)$ from the normal to the face have to be considered for buildings with flat roofs, there is only an advantage to be gained if the distances from the sea and into town or the topography are advantageous. It is shown in Diagram 3.1 that advantages from the use of the directional factor alone give little benefit. This is the reason for the advice earlier that, it the Standard method is used for the derivation of values of Pressure Coefficient, then omnidirectional values should be used. If the roof is asymmetric and the building can be oriented so that the weakest winds blow on the face which gives the greatest forces in the members, then there are advantages in using Directional values in the Standard method.

polygonal, it would probably be worth using the Directional method for Wind Speeds too.

Walls

The Standard method considers only a rectangular or circular building with vertical walls, re-entrant corners, recessed bays and internal wells together with irregular flush faces and inset storeys. Figures 12, 13, 14 and 15 should be studied to see whether data are supplied for the walls under consideration.

To assist the reader to make his choice, values of Pressure Coefficient have been calculated for a simple rectangular shape by the Standard and Directional methods, and the results are shown on pp. 99–101. Clearly there is little to be gained in the relative magnitude of the values and the calculation time factor is about 30 to 1. This ratio is created by the fact that, in addition to the extra cases to be studied, in the Directional method, the values of Pressure Coefficient for the study of 'Overall Loads' is obtained from Table 5 and for the loads on the faces of the building from Table 26. The work is greater than at first appears because the values of Pressure Coefficient in all the zones in Table 26 of the Directional method, are given for values for D/H ratios of 1 and 4 and interpolation has to be made in many values used. Because the value of D/H varies with Wind Direction (although, for different wind directions, the same value of θ may occur on all the faces) the values of Pressure Coefficient have to be calculated afresh for the different value of D/H on each face. In comparison, in the Standard method, the value of Pressure Coefficient for Front and Rear faces depends on D/H only, and that on the Side faces depends only on B; and B and D are equal to either of the Body Dimensions L or W for each case.

For a building with a recessed bay the comparisons are made on pp. 104–109 and the ratio of time spent is even greater.

It would appear that, if data are available from the Standard method, they should be used. As a result of a great number of calibration exercises the authors of the Code have ensured that these values are conservative but only very slightly so.

Roofs

The Standard method only provides data for buildings of rectangular and circular planform. Data for flat roofs (with parapet, or curved or mansard eaves), with or without an inset storey, monopitch, duopitch, hipped, mansard and multi-pitched roofs and free-standing canopy roofs are presented. Figures 16 to 24 should be studied to see whether data are supplied for the roof under consideration. This is a much greater coverage than provided by CP3. It should also be noted that some data in CP3 are now excluded.

Calculation time is also of interest as well as accuracy in those cases where the calculation can be done by either method. Data for complex planforms are not given in the Standard method *per se*, but designers can synthesize complex shapes from rectangular ones as they have done in the past: accurate data are only available in the Directional method. However the simplicity of the Tables in the Standard method, for example Table 8 for the flat roof, conceals the great amount of work which has to be carried out in a desktop calculation. The time consuming part of the Directional method is the evaluation of the areas of the different zones; this can best be done on a scale drawing of the plan, as, for example, on p. 129 for a complex plan-form. At least the calculation of the sizes of zones need only be done once for all wind directions as the scaling length 'b' is a function of L or W in both methods.

In the case of the Directional method permission is given in Section 3.3.2.1.2 to treat a flat, or near flat rectangular roof as a monopitch roof and use the procedures of Section 3.3.3.3.3. To illustrate the possible approaches, the load on a rectangular roof has been calculated by all three methods and the results are presented on pp. 99–101. The reader can make his own comparisons.

Step 5 Pick-and-mix 2

For buildings of a shape for which data are not available in the Standard method, then the Directional method for pressure coefficients must be used. When there is a decision still to be taken, there are four official choices, and one from this Handbook:

 (i)   Standard Wind Speed and Standard Pressure Coefficient.
 (ii) Directional Wind Speed and Standard Pressure Coefficient.
(iii) Standard Wind Speed and Directional Pressure Coefficient.
 (iv) Directional Wind Speed and Directional Pressure Coefficient.
 (v)   'Handbook Best Buy'. Directional pressures and modified Directional Wind Speeds. See below.

The alternatives when ranked in order of complexity (and therefore time of execution) are (i), (ii), (iii), (v) and (iv). The choice can be determined by the sophistication required. For example, in an outline study for a project when orders of magnitude are acceptable, choice (i) would obviously be the correct choice. Again, at the detail design stage when the wind loading is critical, and any reduction would be welcome, then options (iv) or (v) should be chosen.

Alternatives (i) and (iv) are straightforward and their implementation requires the appropriate part of the Code to be followed carefully. In the hybrid combinations, guidance is given in Section 3.4. If option (iii) is considered, then Section 3.4.1 should be read; if option (ii), which is not recommended in this Handbook, then Section 3.4.2 should be read. In both cases the rules must be carefully followed. Option (v) is discussed below.

If option (ii) or (iii) has been chosen after reading the sections above on choice of method for calculating pressure coefficient and wind speed, and after Sections 3.4.1 or 3.4.2 have been read, some additional words of warning are given here.

The major non-conformity between the two methods is the treatment of the Size factor. In the Standard method all wind speeds, and consequently dynamic pressure, are calculated for a 5 m panel and the Size Factor (C_a) adjustment is applied at the conversion from values of Pressure Coefficient into values of Pressure (Section 2.1.3). In the Directional method the values of wind speed have a Size Factor built in through the Gust Factor (g_t) and no further allowance for size is made at the conversion from values of Pressure Coefficient to values of Pressure. In the hybrid situation confusion must be avoided *and it is important to ensure that the Size Adjustment is included once and only once.*

Option (v) is a Handbook interpretation of the Code provisions and is as follows: the Directional method should be used to calculate the wind speed, but only for three values of the diagonal 'a', the panel (5 m), the internal volume, and the Minimal Face Size. The Minimal Face Size is the diagonal 'a' of the smallest face. When the wind speed is required for any other diagonal 'a' value, then the Minimal Face Size wind speed is used *but is corrected at the load calculation stage* for the correct size of the face, or the 'combined faces', by using the Size Effect Factor from the Standard method. The sizes of all the faces are used in the load calculation phase, so that the data required for the correction are already in the programme, providing that the value of C_a and the slope of the curve in Figure 4 (which can change with wind direction) are also available with the wind data. The Directional Pressure Coefficient data are used.

To show the effect of converting Pressure Coefficients to value of pressure, a series of comparisons of loads using options (i) and (v) and based on a Standard Distorted Topography, defined on pp. 96–97, are presented on p. 110 ff.

Step 6   Evaluation of loads

Once the selection of methods has been agreed, the evaluation of values of External Pressure Coefficient is the first task. This is done before the evaluation of values of wind speed because the Pressure Coefficients refer to a Reference Height which appears on the figures in the Code defining the zones. If the 'division by parts' option is being used, several different values of reference height will be chosen. Values of Effective Height are derived from the values of Reference Height using the rules of Section 1.7.3 and it is for all these heights that values of Wind Speed are required and *they should be listed at this stage.*

If the Standard values of Pressure Coefficient are to be used, then the values of Pressure Coefficient are presented in Table 5 for walls (see Figures 11 to 15) and Tables 8 to 15 for roofs (see Figures 16 to 24). If the Directional values are to be used, data are presented in Table 5 (see Figure 30) for Overall Loads, in Tables 26 to 29 for walls (see Figures 31 to 34) and Tables 30 to 36 for roofs (see Figures 35 to 42). Values of Internal Pressure Coefficients are presented in Tables 16 to 19 for both methods;

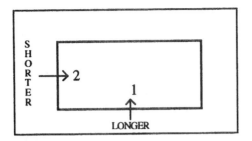

Diagram 1.4

data for long elements and free standing walls are detailed in Tables 20 and 21 (see Figures 25 to 28). Data for circular buildings are given in Table 7.

In this *Handbook* it is recommended that average values of Pressure Coefficient are evaluated for every face of the building, such as shown on p. 102. This not only allows comparison to be made between the values from different methods, but facilitates the derivation of loads at the suitable time.

In the Standard method all calculations are based on two orthogonal directions which are defined in Figures 12a and 16a for a rectangular building. In the case of buildings with asymmetric roofs, the orthogonal directions will be the same as the faces of the smallest enclosing rectangle, but positive and negative forces will be different. Throughout the next paragraphs, orthogonal axes or directions will refer to these directions.

Choice

Convert the choices you have made for solving your problem into a 3 letter 'word' using the flow chart below. One letter must be taken from each stage, thus; **ACE** is a calculation of panel loads (**E**) using the Standard method for the calculation of both values of Pressure Coefficient (**A**) and Wind Speed (**C**).

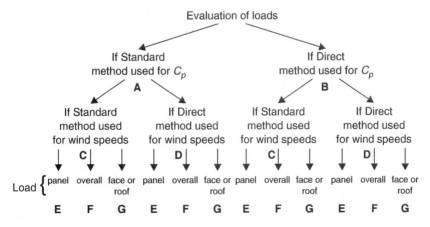

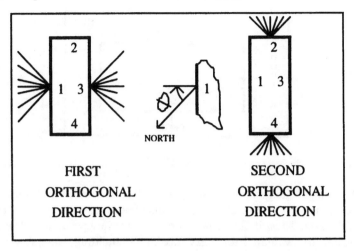

Diagram 1.5

To save time by avoiding reading comments not applicable to your problem, follow these rules: start by reading the paragraph which is headed by the first letter of your 'word'. Read on until a paragraph is headed by two letters. Skip until you reach a paragraph which is headed by the first two letters of your 'word'. Read on until you reach a paragraph headed by three letters. Skip until the paragraph headed by the three leters of your 'word' is reached: read it and end at the next paragraph headed by three letters.

Repeat for your next problem.

A   → *If the Standard method is used for Pressure Coefficients,* then values of wind speed must be calculated at all the required values of Effective Height. The first value of wind speed must be the largest value for a range of directions within ±45° of the first orthogonal direction, and a second value for wind directions between 180° ± 45° of the same. Third and fourth values of wind speed must be calculated within the same limits of the second orthogonal direction. If the roof is symmetric, then the maximum value of the first two values and the maximum value of the third and fourth values will be used for the appropriate orthogonal direction. If not, then three (the maximum over the symmetric direction) or four values should be used. Because of the large number of wind directions (24) covered in the calculation of the two, three or four wind speeds, the directional factor has little effect (see p. 73) and *it is recommended in this Handbook that only the 'omnidirectional' values are calculated,* unless there is a geographical (closeness to sea and/or distance into town) advantage to be gained.

However, if directional values are to be calculated, the following procedure should be followed (see Diagram 1.5 above). For the first orthogonal direction, say $\theta°$ EON, the 'wind speed', whether chosen to be calculated by the Standard or Directional method, is calculated in 15° steps in the range of wind directions of $\theta° \pm 45°$, and the maximum value of the 7 readings taken. The process is repeated for the range of wind directions of $\theta° + 180° \pm 45°$ and the maximum value of the 7 values computed. This means that wind speeds for 24 different wind directions have to be evaluated. If the roof is symmetrical, then the maximum value of the two values is recorded and used. The process is repeated for the second orthogonal direction. This gives either one or two values of wind speed for each orthogonal direction. The process is repeated for every effective height required.

The values of Effective Wind Speed are converted into the value of Dynamic Pressure by the expression in Section 1.3.2.1, $viz.$ $q = 0.5 \times \rho \times V^2 = 0.613 \times V^2$. This is repeated for every Effective Height required.

AC   ⇉ *If the Standard method is used for Wind Speeds,* then the values of 'wind speed' mentioned above are derived in Section 5.4.2 for a panel of size 5 m and, when converted into values of dynamic pressure, are called q_s.

ACE   *If panel loads* are to be calculated, the external load on the panel is equal to the minimum local value of the External Pressure Coefficient (−1.3), multiplied by the area of the panel, by the dynamic pressure (q_s) and by the value of the Size Factor (C_a) appropriate to the size of the panel. In addition, unless the values determined above are values of net pressure coefficient (which are differences across surfaces), values of the internal load on the panel have to be obtained. Values of Internal Pressure Coefficient are presented in Tables 16 to 19 for both methods. A value of internal pressure is obtained by multiplying a value of the Internal Pressure Coefficient by the dynamic pressure (q_s), by the area of the panel and the Size Factor (C_a) appropriate to the internal volume of the building or storey of the building if this is sealed. If the value of Internal Pressure Coefficient has been chosen for a 'Dominant Opening', then the value of Effective Wind Speed, and hence Dynamic Pressure, should be determined for the Effective Height of the wall containing the dominant opening, see Fig. 1.7 below. The net load on the panel is the difference between the external and internal loads.

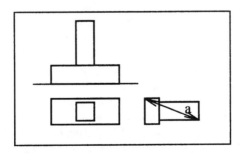

Diagram 1.6

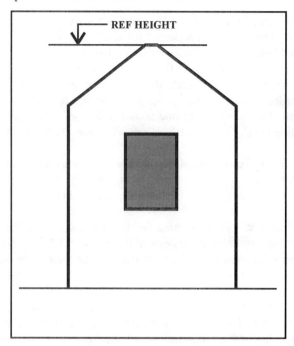

Diagram 1.7

ACF   *If overall loads* are to be calculated, then the value of Pressure Coefficient for the front face (Table 5) is multiplied by the area of the face, by the dynamic pressure (q_s) and by the Size Factor (C_a) for the diagonal *'a'* of the 'Combined Faces' (see Figure 5b) of the building. *The Combined Faces is the minimum of all the Combined Faces of the whole building for all wind directions.* The calculation is repeated for the Rear face. The overall wall load is the sum of the Front and Rear (algebraic) loads multiplied by 0.85. For non-flat roofs, the loads on parts of the roof are calculated in turn by multiplying the value of external pressure coefficient by the area of that part of the roof, by the dynamic pressure (q_s) and by the Size Factor (C_a) for the Combined Faces of the whole building, are resolved into the horizontal orthogonal direction being studied and summed to represent the Overall Roof load in that orthogonal direction. The overall loads on walls and roof are added. This process is repeated for the second orthogonal direction. *A third horizontal loading case has to be considered, which represents the wind onto a corner of the building and is calculated as follows. The stresses in all the structure members are calculated for each of the two, three or four orthogonal cases separately and each member is required to withstand 80% of the sum of the stresses in that member from any two adjacent orthogonal cases occurring simultaneously.* For vertical overall loads, the internal load on the roof has to be considered. This is calculated by multiplying the value of Internal Pressure Coefficient by the area of the roof, by the dynamic pressure (q_s) for the Effective Height of the building, or of the dominant opening if there is one, and by the Size Factor (C_a) for the internal volume. The vertical load in each orthogonal direction is the difference between the sum of the vertical components of all parts of the roof for that orthogonal direction and the internal load; the factor 0.85 is *not* applied to vertical loads.

ACG   *If face or roof loads* are to be calculated, then the external load is equal to the value of the average External Pressure Coefficient on the face (Table 5) multiplied by the area of the face, by the dynamic pressure (q_s) and by the Size Factor (C_a) appropriate to the diagonal '*a*' of the face as defined in Figure 5. The internal load shall equal the product of the Internal Pressure Coefficient, the dynamic pressure (q_s), the area of the face and the size factor (C_a) appropriate to the internal volume. The load on the face is the difference between the External and Internal loads.

AD   ⇉ *If the Directional method is used for Wind Speeds.* This is not recommended for hand calculations in this Handbook, because the increase in accuracy does not justify the work involved. However, if this method is to be used, follow the procedure above interpreting the values of 'wind speed' as the values for a diagonal '*a*' of 5 m at the effective height.

B   → *If the Directional method is used for Pressure Coefficients*, then values of effective wind speed have to be calculated for 12 wind directions and be converted into values of dynamic pressure by the expression given in Section 3.1.2.1 *viz.* $q = 0.5 \times \rho \times V^2 = 0.613 \times V^2$

BC   *If the Standard method is used for Wind Speeds*, then there will be one value of Dynamic Pressure for each wind direction for each effective height,

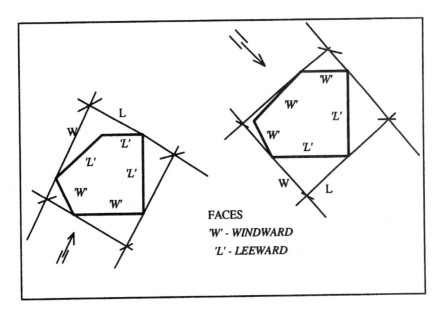

FACES

'W' - WINDWARD

'L' - LEEWARD

Diagram 1.8

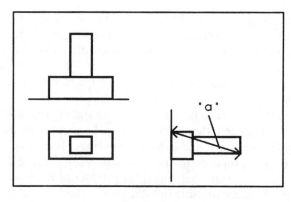

Diagram 1.9

which could be the effective height of the building, or a section of the building. This value is called q_s in each instance.

BCE   *If panel loads* are required, then the external load on the panel is obtained by multiplying the maximum value of Pressure Coefficient (-1.3) by the Area of the panel, by the dynamic pressure (q_s) and by the Size Factor C_a based upon the panel size. In addition, unless the values determined above are values of net pressure coefficient (which are differences across surfaces), values of the internal load on the panel have to be obtained. The internal load on the panel is obtained by multiplying the value of Internal Pressure Coefficient by the dynamic pressure (q_s), by the area of the panel and by the value of Size Factor (C_a) for the internal volume. The procedure is repeated for every wind direction.

BCF   *If overall loads* are required, then each wind direction has to be considered separately. All faces have to be designated either 'Windward' or 'Leeward' depending upon whether they are in front of or behind the points of maximum width *for the wind direction under consideration.* For Windward faces the value of External Pressure Coefficient shall be the value in Table 5 for front faces multiplied by the cosine of the angle between the wind direction and the normal to the face. Thus the value of the external pressure coefficient over the range $1 < D/H > 4$ is $[0.8 - \{(D/H) - 1\}/15] \cos\theta$ where θ is the angle between the wind direction and the normal to the face, *D is the inwind depth and is equal to the smaller of L and W in Figure 30,* and *H* is the height of the building. For Leeward faces the value of External Pressure Coefficient over the range $1 < D/H > 4$ shall be that in Table 5 for Rear faces; *viz.* $[-0.3 + \{(D/H) - 1\}/15]$, where *D* and *H* have the same meaning (note the absence of the $\cos\theta$ term). For a given wind direction the component of Load in the Along-Wind direction shall equal the summation for all faces of the product of the external pressure coefficient on the face with the component of Area of the Face normal to the wind direction ($A \cos\theta$), the dynamic pressure (q_s) and the size factor (C_a) based upon the diagonal 'a' of the combined Faces of the building. *The 'combined* *faces' is the minimum of all the 'combined faces' of the whole building for all wind directions.* For the same wind direction the component of load in the 'Cross-Wind' direction is calculated as above except that the component of area along the wind direction $(A \sin \theta)$ is used in place of the cross-wind component $(A \cos \theta)$. These two components are resolved into the components of load relative to the axes of the building $(F_x$ and $F_y)$. This gives values for the components of overall wall loads which is then multiplied by 0.85. If the roof is non-flat, then the horizontal components of the roof load have to be added to these wall loads. The External Load is calculated for each part of the roof by multiplying the average value of Pressure Coefficient of part of the roof (the sum of the products of Pressure Coefficient for a zone of the roof and the area of the zone divided by the area of the part of the roof) by the area of that part of the roof, by the dynamic pressure (q_s) and by the size factor (C_a) for the *'combined faces' of the building*. This External Load on part of the roof is resolved into horizontal components of load in the x and y directions. The components of load in the x and y directions for the walls and all parts of the roof, taking account of sign, are summed to obtain the components of overall force for that wind direction. The overall vertical load is equal to the difference in external and internal vertical loads. The external vertical load is calculated by taking the sum of the vertical components of the loads on parts of the roof as calculated above (vertical loads are *not* multiplied by 0.85). The internal load, is equal to the product of the value of Internal Pressure Coefficient, the dynamic pressure (q_s), the plan area of the roof and the value of the Size Factor (C_a) based upon the internal volume of the building. Funnelling cannot be taken into account in this method. Correction for mildly-dynamic buildings (C_r) is made at this point. The procedure is repeated for every wind direction.

BCG   *If face or roof loads* are required, then the external load on the face or roof is calculated by multiplying the average value for the pressure coefficient for the face or roof by the dynamic pressure (q_s), by the area of the face or roof and by the value of the Size Factor (C_a) for the face or roof considered (it will be different for faces of different sizes). A value of the internal load on the face or roof is equal to the value of the Internal Pressure Coefficient multiplied by the dynamic pressure (q_s) by the area of the face or roof and by the Size Factor (C_a) for the internal volume. The net face load is equal to the difference between the External and Internal loads.

BD   ⇉ *If the Directional method is used for wind speeds*, then, under option (v), values of dynamic pressure for the three values of diagonal '*a*' (panel, internal and minimal face) are calculated for 12 wind directions at all values of effective height. The value for the Minimal Face is the value based upon diagonal '*a*' for the smallest face of the building, as defined in Figure 5. If options (ii) or (iv) are chosen, the values of the dynamic pressure for a panel, the internal volume, the Combined Faces (see under overall loads later in this section), and each of the face sizes for 12 wind directions and at every value of Effective Height must be calculated.

BDE   *If panel loads* are to be derived, then the panel load is equal to the maximum local value of the Pressure Coefficient (−1.3) multiplied by the dynamic pressure appropriate to the diagonal *'a'* of the panel evaluated at the effective height and by the area of the panel; this gives a value of the external load on the panel. In addition, unless the values determined above are values of net pressure coefficient (which are differences across surfaces), values of the internal load on the panel have to be obtained. The value of internal load is equal to the product of the value of internal pressure coefficient, the area of the panel and the dynamic pressure based on diagonal *'a'* for the internal volume or storey. The height at which this dynamic pressure is calculated is the effective height of the wall containing the dominant opening, if there is one, otherwise it is the effective height of the top of the building. The net face load is equal to the difference between the external and internal loads. The procedure is repeated for every wind direction.

BDF   *If overall loads* are required, then each wind direction has to be considered separately. All faces have to be designated either 'Windward' or 'Leeward' depending upon whether they are in front of or behind the points of maximum width *for the wind direction under consideration.*

For Windward faces the value of External Pressure Coefficient shall be the value in Table 5 for front faces multiplied by the cosine of the angle between the wind direction and the ingoing normal to the face. Thus, for values $1 < D/H > 4$ the value of external pressure coefficient is $[0.8 - \{(D/H) - 1\}/15]\cos\theta$ where θ is the angle between the wind direction and the normal to the surface, D *is the inwind depth and is equal to the smaller of L and W in Figure 30*, and H is the height of the building. For

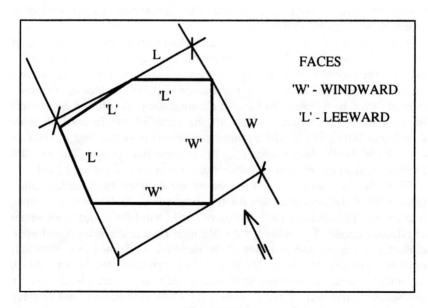

Diagram 1.10

leeward faces the value of external pressure coefficient shall be that in Table 5 for Rear faces; *viz.* $[-0.3 + \{(D/H) - 1\}/15]$, where D and H have the same meaning and D/H has the same limitations (note the absence of the cos θ term). For a given wind direction the component of Load in the 'Along-Wind' direction shall equal the summation for all faces of the product of the External Pressure Coefficient on the face with the component of area of the face normal to the wind direction $(A \cos \theta)$ the dynamic pressure (q_s) and the Size Factor (C_a) for the diagonal 'a' for the 'combined faces' of the building. *The 'combined faces' is the minimum of all the 'combined faces' of the whole building for all wind directions.* For the same wind direction the component of Load in the Cross-Wind direction is calculated as above except that the component of Area along the wind direction $(A \sin \theta)$ is used in place of the cross-wind component $(A \cos \theta)$. These two components are resolved into the components of load relative to the axes of the building $(F_x$ and $F_y)$. This gives values for the components of overall wall loads which are then multiplied by 0.85. If the roof is non-flat, then the components of horizontal roof load have to be added to these wall loads. The External Load is calculated for each part of the roof by multiplying the average value of Pressure Coefficient of that part of the roof (the sum of the products of Pressure Coefficient for a zone of the roof and the area of the zone divided by the area of the part of the roof) by the area of that part of the roof, by the dynamic pressure based on the Combined Faces. This External Load on part of the roof is resolved into horizontal components of load in the x and y directions summed for all parts of the roof and added to the components of the wall loads. The overall vertical load is equal to the difference in external and internal vertical loads. The external load is calculated by taking the sum of the vertical components of the loads on parts of the roof as calculated above. The internal load, is equal to the product of the value of Internal Pressure Coefficient, the dynamic pressure based on the internal volume of the building and the plan area of the roof. Funnelling cannot be taken into account in this method. Correction for the mildly-dynamic (C_r) behaviour of the building is applied at this point. The procedure is repeated for every wind direction.

BDG   *If face or roof loads* are required, the value of the diagonal 'a' used is the diagonal as defined on Figure 5 for the face. In the Directional method this would require an additional calculation of dynamic pressure for each face which is of a different size; a large task. However, option (v), recommended in this *Handbook* uses the dynamic pressure for the Minimal Face, corrected by the Size Effect Factor (C_a) for the size of the face or roof. To obtain the External Face or Roof load, this dynamic pressure is multiplied by the mean value of the Pressure Coefficient for the face or roof, and by the area of the face or roof. A value of the internal load on the wall or roof is calculated by multiplying a value of Internal Pressure Coefficient by the dynamic pressure appropriate to the internal volume and by the area of the roof as for the panel load. The net face load is equal to the difference between the External and Internal loads. The procedure is repeated for every wind direction.

Steps useful for frequent users

It is assumed here that the frequent user is familiar with the remarks for the infrequent user; in this part, details of the author's approach to providing procedures in as convenient a form as possible (short of programming the whole Code) for the frequent user of the Code are described. These are the programs which the author has written in anticipation of providing results, both for this Handbook and for using the Code himself for design applications.

  However, before embarking on the details, three general points will be made

  (i)   If you are going to write a complete computer program, then write one for options (iv) or (v) because it will not be much more complex than the program for the Standard method.
 (ii)   Allowance for funnelling in the Directional method can easily be made in the calculation of Panel loads: it is very difficult to make the allowance in face loads, because it requires exact information of the position of the neighbouring building with respect to the face of the building under consideration. If in doubt, assume the worst and increase the suction in zone A. It cannot be used for Overall loads.
(iii)   It is recommended that option (v) is used. This is explained on p. 7.

And now for the author's approach.

  If nothing else is done, it is recommended that a program is written to derive wind speeds as this calculation has to be performed so many times, and the program is relatively simple to write. However the BRE program 'Strongblow' is commercially available to perform these calculations.

Wind speeds

It is almost as simple to write a program which will calculate wind speeds for both the Standard and Directional approach as for either individually; so it is suggested that this is done: it is required for option (v) anyway. It is recommended that the wind speeds are calculated for the standard wind directions of North and every 30° therefrom (see end of this paragraph), and that a pair of subroutines (the author uses 'Spline' and 'Splint', but any others are just as good) which will fit curves to numerical data and obtain values of the various variables ($Sb,$ etc.) for specific values of distance from the sea and into town. The data from Tables 3, 4, 22, 23 and 24 are fed in as data statements and values for each variable are calculated in turn, and finally the value of Effective Wind Speed is calculated. It is recommended here that whether the correction for wind direction is entered or not is at the request of the user during the running of the program. This means that the same calculation procedure will produce data for 12 wind directions with different distances from the sea and into town for each, *or* the data for 12 wind directions with the same distances from the sea and into town, *or* the data for 12 different distances from the sea and into town with no indication of direction relative to North.

The output of the program can be in several forms; some which present the data in the form illustrated in Group 1 of Chapter 3 of this Handbook, but especially one which presents the values of wind speed with no embellishments. This last form will be called up in all the later programs for wall and roof loads. It is recommended that this output has seven rows of values for each of the 12 columns; the columns, which, for future use, are the standard 12 wind directions (0°, 30°, etc.) and the whole data are for a given value of Reference Height. The first three rows are data for the Directional method and represent three different diagonal 'a' values, specified in order (in the author's program they are for Panel, Internal Volume and Minimal Face). The remaining rows are for the Standard method. The fourth and fifth rows are for values of diagonal 'a' for panel and internal volume: the sixth row are the slope of the appropriate curve in Figure 4, and the seventh row are the value of C_a appropriate to the Minimal Face.

These data are used in all future programs. If required, the output could be presented in another file, formatted with headings and details so that it could be presented in its own right in the report of the calculations.

It pays to store the input data in another file, so that they (for instance 12 values of distances from sea and into town), can be called down to calculate wind speeds for different values of H or diagonal 'a' without requiring re-entry.

Wall loads

In the Standard method only rectangular buildings need be programmed; for these two possibilities to occur, either the wind direction relative to the

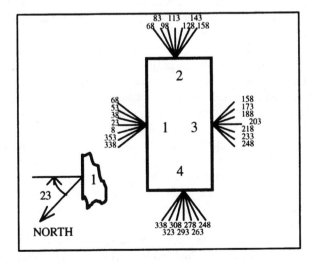

Diagram 1.11

faces is known or not. *If the wind direction is not known*, then the maximum of the values for the 12 wind directions must be calculated for four different values of the diagonal 'a', the panel, the internal, and up to four face sizes. The wind program has calculated the first two and given the slope of the appropriate curve in Figure 4, so that the values of wind speed for the two face sizes can be obtained from the value for the panel by multiplying by the appropriate value of C_a, calculated from the slope of the Figure 4 curve given as part of the output of the wind program. Two cases are studied for overall loads, using the maximum wind speed for the diagonal 'a' appropriate to each face in turn. *If the wind direction is known*, then the maximum value of wind speed over *four* ranges (for wind directions in 15° steps over the range ±45° from the normal to the face, seven steps in all); the four ranges apply to the four faces. This is best carried out in the 'walls' program by interpolation from the data from the 'Wind' program because any angle between face 1 and North can be allowed for (it need not be a multiple of 15°). The calculation is repeated for the four values of diagonal 'a' (notice that the slope of the curve in Figure 4 may change with wind direction); eight times 24 values, and data on loads, or pressures, for four cases ($+$ and $-$ loads in the x and y directions) are presented (although the opposing faces are the same size, the wind speeds within ±45° of opposing faces can be different). See the example on p. 112.

   In the Directional method any shaped building with any number of faces can be considered. *For Overall loads*, the expression in Paragraph 3.1.3.3.2 should be programmed. This requires the determination of which are 'front' and 'rear' faces. The way this has been done by the author is to input the length and inclination of all the faces (relative to the x-axis). The origin of the x,y plane is taken as the starting point of face 1. The co-ordinates of the other corners can be determined, first in terms of (x,y) and then in terms of (r, θ). The co-ordinates of the corners in any other plane (ξ, η), which has the same origin as the (x,y) plane, but based on wind axes are easily determined by increasing θ by the change in wind direction. It is a simple matter to determine the 'front' and 'rear' faces and also the values of L and W in the (ξ, η) plane (see Figure 30a), because this is the wind plane. For Panel and Surface (or Face) Loads, the data of Tables 26 and 27 have to be used. In the determination of the overall loads, the value of D has been calculated for each wind direction. It is recommended that the value of pressure coefficient is calculated for the zones A, B, C and D for values of D/H of both 1 and 4 for the correct wind direction, and the required value is determined by interpolation for the correct value of D/H. The allocation of zone A requires that the 'front facing' corner of the face has to be chosen. This can be determined by the sign of the angle between the wind direction and the normal to the face. A knowledge of which is the 'front facing corner' is necessary in the evaluation of the Reduction Factor in Table 27. To conform strictly with the Code, the value of wind speed for every face has to be calculated from a value of the Gust Factor (g_t), but it is recommended here option (v) is used and that the value of the diagonal 'a' for the 'minimal face' value mentioned in the calculation of Wind Speeds above, is used as a basis, and that the value for all the other faces is derived from that using the Size Effect Factor of the Standard Method (C_a). For this purpose the sixth and seventh rows of data were provided in the program for wind speeds above, so that a value of (C_a) for the diagonal 'a' for every face can be calculated quickly.

For the first time in any Code, the effect of 'funnelling' the flow between the building in question and its neighbour is quantified. The rules can be incorporated easily in the program for the Standard method, but not so easily in the program for the Directional method. It is recommended in this Handbook that this correction is written into the Standard method in full (that is to say that its effect on both the 'panel' and 'side wall' loads are calculated). In the Directional method the effect should be included in the calculation of panel loads, which can be significant, but is omitted from the calculation of the load on side faces; it cannot be included for overall loads. The reason for this is that the amount of data required about the relative positions of the two or more buildings is complex and is difficult to include in a 'general' program.

When the amount of work involved in even a Standard calculation is appreciated, and when a computer program is written for both methods, then the Directional one may be used in every case.

The time involved in debugging a program can be large, so it is recommended here that programs for vertical walls are programmed, and that, on the infrequent occasions when non-vertical walls are encountered, then a hand calculation will be satisfactory. If their use is to be frequent, then the procedure is similar to the above because the format of Tables 28 and 29 is similar to that for Table 26 and the original program can be copied with the new data replacing the original data and extra questions about the angle of the wall added (note the different wind direction intervals).

A program to calculate wall loads on buildings with re-entrant corners and internal wells is complex. However, in writing the program for normal walls, it is possible to write the values of pressure coefficient for the different zones for different angles of the wall to North into a separate file and use these data in a manual calculation for re-entrant corners on the odd occasion when this problem arises.

Roof loads

A complete program can be written to calculate the loads on flat roofs, but the author of this Handbook considers that it is not worth the complexity. It is recommended, however, that a hybrid approach is used. Two programs have been written by the author, to be used separated by some manual work. The first accepts data on the Number of Faces, the angle of the normal from face 1 East of North, and the angles of the other faces relative to face 1. In the program values of the wind direction normal to the face and the pressure coefficients in the six zones A to F for the wind direction relative to each 'front face' are calculated for the North wind. The procedure is repeated for the other 11 standard (every 30°) wind directions. Also at the foot of the table are printed the number of faces which are 'front facing' faces for each wind direction. A typical table is shown on p. 130.

The next part of the procedure is manual. A plan of the roof is drawn twelve times on a sheet of A4 tracing paper, each drawing representing a different wind direction from North to 330°. The first drawing is placed over graph paper with an axis of the graph paper aligned along the wind direction and the cross-wind breadth (B) is measured. The Scaling length (b) is determined as the lesser of B or $2H$, the zones are drawn on the tracing paper, and their areas measured. The procedure is repeated for all the 'front facing' faces, the number of which are presented at the foot of the first computer table. The 12 drawings of the roof are completed in the same way, and the areas noted. See the example on p. 131.

The second program takes the values of pressure coefficient from the first program (an unembellished version has been stored for the purpose), has as input the total area of the roof, a factor for the loads, and the areas of the zones previously measured and presents the results in the format of p. 131. The areas are printed formally in this output for inclusion in the report; the interesting data are the values of the average pressure coefficient for the roof and the values of the load for every wind direction.

2

Section by section interpretation of the Code

This part is divided into a section by section examination of the Code. Any perceived uncertainties are clarified and an extended index is provided so that a specific operation in the Code can be located quickly.

Contents

The contents list gives the section headings and the main subsection headings for the Code and its Annexes.

Foreword

The most important technical comment here is to state that the wind speeds on the map of this Code are *hourly-average values over open flat level ground with a ground roughness height of 0.03 m which have a probability of 1/50 of being exceeded in any one year.* This is different from CP3 in which a 3-second average value of wind speed was the starting point, whereas in the present Code, the hourly-average value of wind speed is the starting point. This accounts for the much smaller values on the map in this Code, which do not represent a drastic reduction in the wind speeds, and therefore wind loads as compared with CP3. It is essential that Map Wind Speeds from this Code are not used directly in place of values of Map Wind Speeds in CP3. This new approach is also used in BS 8100.

The main reason for the change is that when wind blows over hills, the mean (hourly-average) wind speeds are changed, but the turbulence is not. Thus, if speed-ups are to be calculated accurately, it must be possible to separate the mean from the fluctuating part. A secondary reason is that the hourly-average wind speed is the starting point for fatigue and dynamic calculations, so, when and if a dynamic part is added to this Code, the wind speed data in this Code can be used. A further practical consideration for this change is that the European Code of Practice uses a 10-minute averaging period but for a ground roughness of 0.05 m. The resulting values of map wind speed are very similar to those in this Code.

The statement that '. . . the mean basic wind speed is subsequently converted into a gust wind speed for use in design *(by a gust peak factor which takes account of gust duration time, height of structure above the ground and the size of the structure'* is only true for the Directional method; the fact that two different methods are detailed in the Code is not mentioned until the next paragraph.

The next paragraph explains that structures which respond to the wind in a dynamic fashion (often called 'wind sensitive structures') are not covered by the Code, and, for the first time in a British Code, a calculation procedure is given to identify such structures. This paragraph should have appeared at the top of this Section. These remarks are extended in Section 1.1 both in the Code and this Handbook.

The two methods of calculation permitted by the Code are called 'Standard' and 'Directional'. In the Code the order is always Standard–Directional, which is a pity because the Directional method is the basic one, which has been simplified to reduce the amount of work required in its implication.

In the Standard method in this Code the change in value of wind speed from hourly-average to the correct averaging time for a 5 m panel is contained in the S_b factor (Section 5.4.2.1) and further corrected to any other panel size by the C_a factor (Section 4.5.1.4) during the calculation of pressure, in the calculation of which intensities of turbulence in the atmosphere have been assumed. In the Directional method the mean values of wind speed are changed by a 'Peak Gust Factor', (g_t) (Section A 2.3 and Annex F) to allow for the peak value of wind speed for any panel, face or building size. Because the derivation of t second gust speeds are generated from hourly average values in the present Code, the correction is greater than in CP3 where the old S2 factor corrected from 3-second values. In the Standard method the theoretical correction for topography is impossible, so a unique relation is *assumed* between Gust Speed and Mean Wind Speed and so an allowance for topography is included in the Standard method, which is generally conservative.

For a scientific view on the most appropriate reference wind speed, see Article 1 in Chapter 4.

The last paragraph of the Foreword states: *'Compliance with a British Standard does not of itself confer immunity from legal obligations'*.

Section 1. General

1.1   Scope[1]

The last paragraph in this Section should be read first. In this, structures which are liable to dynamic excitation are exempted from this Code

---

[1] Section numbers in the Code are given in a box before each heading.

(detailed in Section 1.6). For the first time a calculation procedure is given whereby it can be determined if a structure is liable to dynamic excitation (or is 'Wind Sensitive' as it is sometimes called).

If a full dynamic calculation has been performed, the results will show whether the structure will respond dynamically or 'not'. If the answer is 'not', then this Code can be used.

In the absence of a full dynamic calculation, the procedure to be followed in this Code is to calculate the 'dynamic augmentation factor', and, if it exceeds 0.25, or the building exceeds 300 m in height, then it is necessary to assume that the structure is sufficiently dynamic to require a full dynamic analysis and this Code does not apply.

In the references, found after Annex F there is a list of published sources of analysis of dynamic structures. It is more relevant to consult Annex C, which describes and gives the derivation of the 'Dynamic Augmentation Factor' and only to consult the references providing the criteria for mildly-dynamic response are exceeded.

If a whole structure is dynamic it cannot be analysed by the data in this Code. However there is no restriction to the evaluation of panel loads using data in this Code. This is explained in Chapter 1, Step 1 of this Handbook.

The use of the term 'gust peak wind loads' is important. By definition, if a value of a mean pressure coefficient was multiplied by a mean value of dynamic pressure (one half times the air density times the square of the wind speed), then the mean value of pressure would be obtained. It was previously assumed in CP3 that, if a mean pressure coefficient was multiplied by a 3-second-average value of dynamic pressure with a given probability of exceedence, then a 3-second-average value of pressure with the same probability of exceedence would be obtained. This is not altogether accurate. In this Code the values of Pressure Coefficient are values of Peak Pressure Coefficient which have been obtained in a wind tunnel study by dividing the measured value of the peak pressure by the measured value of the peak dynamic pressure for the same averaging time. In practice the latter method yields slightly higher values but is more accurate. It has only been possible to carry out these measurements since computers have been harnessed to wind tunnels.

The choice of method (Standard or Directional) is described in Section 1.8.

In this Section of the Code it would appear that either the Standard or the Directional method should be used in its entirety, this is not so: mixing is allowed in paragraph 1.8.4.

1.3   Definitions

Both the Basic Wind Speed and the Site Wind Speed are hourly-average values of wind speed. This is different from the values in CP3, which were 3-second average values. This is the reason why the numerical values on the map (Figure 6) and the map in CP3 are so different. The transformation to gust speeds takes place in the calculation of the Effective Wind Speed. The allowance for topography is different in the two methods, in that, in the Standard method, it is included in the Site Wind Speed, but in the Directional method, it is allowed for in the conversion from the Site Wind Speed to the Effective Wind Speed. Care must be taken to ensure that it has been allowed for once and only once.

The length of the building is always given the symbol L and the Width of the Building is always given the symbol W. These are Body Dimensions in that they refer to the building and are unchangeable. In the case of an arbitrarily-shaped building, L and W can be the dimensions of the Smallest Enclosing Rectangle or Circle. It is coincidental that the smallest enclosing rectangle is normal to the wind direction in Figure A2(a).

Crosswind breadth is always given the symbol B. Inwind depth is always given the symbol D. These are Wind Dimensions in that they are aligned to the wind and change with wind direction.

1.4   Main symbols

This section lists all the symbols used in the body of the Code, additional symbols are used only in Annexes some of which are defined in the Annex when they appear, the rest are defined in this Handbook.

In parentheses, after each definition, is the reference where each is further defined on a sketch or in an equation.

It is probably a good idea to turn back the corner of this page in the Code so that easy reference can be made to the symbols at any time when reading the rest of the Code.

1.5   Outline of procedure for calculating wind loads

1.5.1

In Stage 2b it is suggested that there is an option of using one of the methods for dynamic analysis *or* conducting a wind tunnel test. These are not alternatives. A wind tunnel model which represents the dynamic performance of a structure is extremely expensive and the study extremely difficult to carry out. The data from a wind tunnel test *on a rigid model* can be fed into a dynamic analysis of the structure, providing that the movements of the structure are not so large, or of such a nature as to change the aerodynamics of the flow around the building; the static study is usually satisfactory. Loading data from this Code could also be fed into a dynamic analysis, providing that there are data in the Code for the shape of structure, and it is given in small enough steps of wind direction, which is most unlikely.

In Stages 4 and 6 the subject of topography is raised. A difficulty arises because the effect of a hill is to change the mean (hourly-average) wind speeds without significantly altering the fluctuating part. In the Standard method, because 'altitude' and 'topography' have something in common, it was considered reasonable by the authors of the Code to combine the corrections into a single factor, and this adjustment is applied when converting Basic Wind Speed (from the map) to Site Wind Speed. (Both of these are hourly-average wind speeds, which is correct for both the altitude and topography corrections; but the subsequent conversion into a gust speed affects both the altitude and topography corrections, which is wrong. However the simplification used is conservative.) In the Directional method the topography correction is made when converting the Site Wind Speed into the Effective Wind Speed, the Altitude correction having already been applied in converting the Map Wind Speed into the Site Wind Speed. Although not producing confusion at the calculation stage, because both operations are separate, it appears odd that the same correction is made at different stages in the two methods, but there are sound reasons for the procedure.

In Stages 8 and 10 the term 'dynamic pressure' occurs. This has nothing to do with the dynamic performance of the building. The term, which is derived from aircraft aerodynamics, represents the pressure energy present in the wind due to its velocity (see paragraph 4.4).

1.5.2

This Section describes the loading on parts of the whole building or structure. Care must be taken to use a value of the 'Effective Wind Speed' appropriate to the height and size of the part whose load is being calculated. Different values of wind speed apply to each part.

1.6   Dynamic classification

This Code does not apply to buildings which respond in a dynamic way to the wind: a full explanation of dynamic response is given in Article 3 on p. 149. In this paragraph the term 'mildly dynamic' is used. To explain this, a resumé must be given of dynamic response. A child's swing builds up amplitude over a series of cycles, absorbing a little energy at each cycle until the energy it absorbs per cycle from the person pushing is equal to the energy it dissipates per cycle in damping (the damping varies with amplitude). The swing is then said to have reached its limit cycle. The same happens to a building, provided that it is able to oscillate, the wind taking the part of the pusher. It is obvious, in such a condition, that the amplitude of the building, and consequently the stresses in the foundations of the building, bear no relation to the instantaneous applied loads but to the stored energy. Consequently any method of analysis which assumes a relationship between stresses in the building and the applied loads will be irrelevant. This is why this Code does not apply to dynamic structures. However, as a result of the stiffness and damping of a building, if a limit cycle is achieved after only one or two cycles, so that the energy stored in the building is very small compared to the work done by the wind in every cycle of loading, then a static analysis is appropriate with a factor to allow for the increase in stress to allow for the small amount of stored energy. Such a building is called 'mildly dynamic' and the Dynamic Augmentation Factor is the factor by which the static stresses must be multiplied to obtain the actual stresses. In this Code the Dynamic Augmentation Factor is called C_r, and the loads are multiplied by $(1 + C_r)$ to allow for it.

If the value of C_r is greater than 0.25 or the building is taller than 300 m, then the building is said to be 'wind sensitive' (which is another way of saying that it responds dynamically to the wind), and this Code does not apply. If the Code does apply, then the value of C_r calculated at this time, should be recorded for future use. Even if this Code does not apply to the whole structure, *it does apply for the calculation of cladding loads.*

1.6.2   Limits of Applicability

The wording 'This Part of BS 6399....' refers to Part 2, as opposed to Part 1 (Live and Dead loads) and Part 3 (Snow loads). It is also hoped that, at a future date, another part of BS 6399 will cover dynamic structures; this is not planned at present. It also suggests that dynamic response is the only limit, there are others. For instance the range of building shapes included, although a vast increase on CP3, is still limited. The other point not made is there can be some very interesting 'interactions' between two buildings if they are in close proximity; this is now covered in this Code by a procedure called 'funnelling' (see Sections 2.4.1.4 and 3.3.1.1.3).

1.7   Site exposure

1.7.1

The height of 10 m for the measurement of Site Wind Speeds was chosen because this is the height which has been standardized by most of the Meteorological Offices around the world for the measurement of wind speed. The open site aspect is also standard because the Meteorological Offices were originally established by Air Ministries for the purpose of assisting flight. They were therefore established on airfields, which are, by definition, open sites.

The Site Wind Speed is the Map wind speed corrected for differences in altitude, direction, seasonal exposure and probability level from the Standard values. The Effective Wind Speed, upon which the Pressure Coefficients are based, depends upon Effective Height, Ground Roughness and Fetch.

1.7.2

In this Code, there are only three descriptions of the roughness of the ground, *viz.*, sea, country and town and all are assumed to be flat. There are separate corrections for hills and escarpments. It might seem odd that there are only three categories, only two on land, when there were four in

CP3 and in the Eurocode; the reason is the importance of fetch, which is explained in the next paragraph.

The wind over the UK blows in from the sea, and, in a very long passage over the sea, the velocity profile (variation of wind speed with height) and turbulence is consistent with a sea undersurface. On reaching land, the additional roughness of the land causes additional friction at the ground, which slows the wind at the ground. With eddy mixing in the earth's boundary layer, this reduction in wind speed and increase in turbulence affect a greater and greater height the greater the length of ground traversed (fetch is the term for the ground upwind), and, if sufficient land were traversed, would attain equilibrium conditions for a surface of the ground's roughness. If this wind, after a distance of country, reaches a town, which is rougher than the country, a new slower and more turbulent layer begins to develop at ground level, affecting greater heights with greater penetration of the town. Once the town is passed, another new layer develops at ground level consistent with country ground roughness, the effect of the town rising in height until its effect is overtaken by the new country profile and turbulence and the effect of the town has vanished. The methods of the present Code allows for these effects in terms of 'Distance from the Sea' and 'Distance into Town'.

1.7.3 | Reference height and effective height

This is a most important Section. The Reference Height is that height on the structure for which the Pressure Coefficient data have been based. The Effective Height is the height at which the values of wind speed will be calculated to convert values of Pressure Coefficient into values of pressure. The difference is due to the sheltering effect of the surrounding buildings. The expressions from which the differences can be calculated are given in Section 1.7.3.3.

1.8 | Choice of method

1.8.1

A structure is considered 'Wind Sensitive' if the value of C_r is greater than 0.25, or its height is greater than 300 m. It is implied in this Section that if the value of C_r is less than 0.25, but if the height of the structure is greater than 100 m, then only the Directional method should be used.

1.8.4

This Section allows the Mixing of the Methods and reference is made to Section 3.4. Reference should also be made to Sections 1.2 and 1.5 of Chapter 1 of this Handbook.

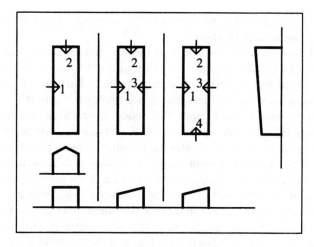

Diagram 2.1

Section 2. Standard method

| 2.1 | **Standard Wind Loads** |

| *2.1.1* | *Wind direction* |

The number of orthogonal cases to be studied depends upon the type of building: only two cases are studied for buildings with flat, or equally duo-pitch or hipped roofs: the wind normal to the faces of the rectangle in turn. The text explains that, if the building is singly-symmetric or asymmetric then three or four cases have to be studied; this can only arise on a rectangular building if it has a non-flat roof. If the asymmetry arises because of a polygonal planform, then, the Pressure Coefficient data have to be obtained from the Directional method, and it is recommended in the last paragraph of this Handbook that the Directional method should be used in that case.

| *2.1.1.2* |

If there are different fetches in the different directions or direction factors are being used, then the first value of wind speed must be the largest value in the range of directions within ±45° of the first orthogonal direction, and a second value for wind directions between 180° ± 45° of the same. Third and fourth values of wind speed must be calculated within the same limits of the second orthogonal direction. If the roof is symmetric, then the maximum value of the first two values and the maximum value of the third and fourth values will be used for the appropriate orthogonal direction, if not, then three (the maximum over the symmetric direction) or four values should be used. Because of the large number of wind directions (24) covered in the calculation of the two, three or four wind speeds, the directional factor has

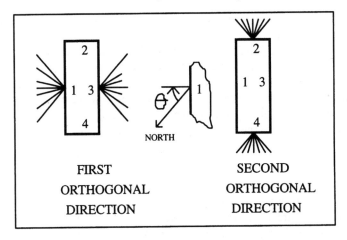

Diagram 2.2

little effect (see p. 73) and *it is recommended in this Handbook that only the 'omnidirectional' values are calculated,* unless there is a geographical (closeness to sea and/or distance into town) advantage to be gained. See Chapter 1 of this Handbook for further information.

2.1.2 | *Dynamic Pressure*

The dynamic pressure is the scaling factor for wind speed and is equal to the effective pressure in energy terms of the wind speed. The relationship between dynamic pressure and wind speed is given in this Section and is $q_s = 0.5 \times \rho \times V_e^2 = 0.613 \times V_e^2$.

In the Standard method the value of Dynamic Pressure is based upon a panel size of 5m and only one value is calculated for every Effective Height for each orthogonal direction (see above). *But different values apply at different Effective Heights and there can be several values of dynamic pressure in an overall calculation.*

2.1.3 | *Wind load*

Notice that the same value of dynamic pressure (q_s) is used for both internal and external pressure. This assumes that the same value of Effective Height applies to the derivation of internal and external pressure. If there is a dominant opening, then the dynamic pressure for internal loads shall be based on the reference dynamic pressure at the Effective Height of the wall in which the dominant opening occurs. Different values of C_a are used to allow for the different areas over which the external pressure is to be correlated and to allow for the internal volume of the building in the calculation of the internal pressure (see Section 2.6 for values of diagonal 'a' for internal volumes).

At the start of Section 2.1.3.3 the value of p is the difference between the values calculated in Sections 2.1.3.1 and 2.1.3.2 for external and internal pressures respectively. In the second part of Section 2.1.3.3 the pressure difference is calculated directly because, for free-standing canopies, the pressure coefficient data are given in terms of pressure differences. This is signified in this Code by the expression *Net Pressure Coefficient*.

2.1.3.4

In Section 2.1.3.4 it is stated that the factor C_a accounts for the non-simultaneous action of gusts: this is not strictly accurate. C_a allows for the range of gusts which are correlated on a surface. All the very large gusts are assumed to engulf a whole surface and the effect of the gust is the same at all points on the surface and the wind speed is said to be correlated over the area of the surface. Small gusts engulf, and are therefore correlated over, small areas. So for a given sized area, there is a range of large gusts which are fully correlated, a range of medium sized gusts which are partially correlated and a range of small gusts which have no effect. The assumption made in the size factor approach is that, for a given size of area, there is a limiting size of gust such that all larger gusts are fully correlated and all smaller gusts are uncorrelated. The choice of value for the limiting gust takes into account the partly correlated ones. In the calculation of overall loads, a factor of 0.85 is used to allow for the uncorrelation of the eddies on different faces separated by a shear layer, because it has been found that a shear layer, the remnant of the boundary layer on a face which flows off from the downstream edge of a face, causes decorrelation of fluctuations on each side of the layer. This is a different phenomenon. The 0.85 factor only applies when loads on opposite faces are added.

Values for the diagonal 'a' are defined in this paragraph, both for external and internal application.

All panels are considered to be of size 5 m or less, unless load-sharing can be demonstrated, in which case the 'effective' size of the panel is larger than the actual size of the panel, and is to be considered equal to the diagonal of the area over which the load is shared. Note that the values of 'a' for internal volumes depends upon whether there is a dominant opening or not.

2.1.3.5

For the calculation of Shear Forces and Bending Moments, the value of the diagonal 'a' is to be that of the loaded area above that of the level considered, as illustrated in Figure 5c. This has implications when using the Directional method and is not mentioned in Section A.1.4.3. The value of wind speed used must be that at the highest part of the loaded area.

In Section 2.1.3.6 there is no mention of the value of diagonal 'a' to be used in the calculation of $\sum P_{front} - \sum P_{rear}$. It is recommended here that a value appropriate to each face is used in the calculation of the value of P for that face.

The factor 0.85 is an empirical factor which allows for the loss of correlation (the simultaneous occurrence) of peak pressures on different faces of a building. The factor 0.85 has been obtained as a result of many calibration exercises. There is also a smaller loss of correlation between the wall and roof loads. For non-flat roofs, the roof load makes a contribution to the horizontal loads but the factor 0.85 should *not* be applied to the roof loads which have been calculated on a value of diagonal '*a*' based on the overall size of the roof. Internal pressure is assumed to be constant within the whole building, and its value is related to either the volume of the building or the storey (if each storey is isolated from its neighbours or to a dominant opening) by the use of an effective value for diagonal '*a*' in the calculation of wind speed. If the area of wall on both sides of the building is the same, the load exerted by the internal pressure cancels out when the overall horizontal load on the building is calculated. The 0.85 factor is not used when the internal pressure is combined with external pressures, because, due to the large value of diagonal '*a*' used in its calculation, it approaches a mean, or long time-average value. The value of '*D*' (which is the inwind depth of the building) used in the calculation of front and rear loads *is the smaller of W or L* and not the actual inwind value.

In Note 2 it is stated that the internal pressure need not be considered in the calculation of overall horizontal loads, the phrases 'when they are of equal size', and 'on level ground' are added in this paragraph. If, however, the walls are of different size, but are on level (horizontal) ground, then the internal pressure on the different size is allowed for in the internal pressure on the sloping roof. Only if the ground is not horizontal does the internal pressure produce a horizontal force.

A possible combination of the loads calculated separately for the two orthogonal cases is discussed at the end of the Section and can produce the design case. Because the loads in the two (or three or four) orthogonal cases occur for different wind directions, they cannot be combined into a Resultant Load. However, when the wind is onto a corner of the building, loads will be imposed in both orthogonal directions. This is accounted for in this Code in the following way. The stresses in all the main members shall be calculated for each (two, three or four) of the orthogonal cases separately. In addition to withstanding these stresses, every member shall be required to withstand the simultaneous imposition of 80 per cent of the sum of the stresses in them from any two orthogonal cases which are for wind directions at right angles, the combination giving the highest load being considered the design case.

| 2.1.3.7 | *Asymmetric loads* |

Even if a building is symmetric, the wind can impose an asymmetric load on it. Thus, even a lower load, if applied asymmetrically, can impose higher

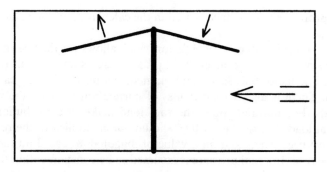

Diagram 2.3

stresses in the members of the building. To allow for this possibility, rules for the withholding of some 40 per cent of the load on one face of a building are given in this paragraph.

2.1.3.8. *Frictional Drag Component*

For long walls and roofs with attached flow over part of their length, the wind can exert a frictional force in the direction of the wind. Not all the surface has attached flow, so the Surface Friction Drag is not applied over the whole of the surfaces of walls and roofs. These forces apply along the surface of the building. These loads should be added to the pressure loads on the structure.

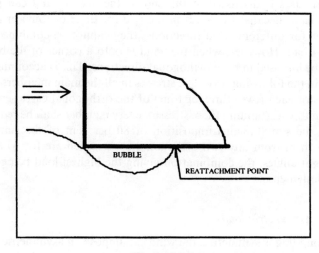

Diagram 2.4

2.2 | Standard wind speeds

2.2.1 | Basic Wind Speed

The basic wind speed is given on the map (Figure 6) and its derivation is explained in Annex B of this Code and in Article 1 of Chapter 4 of this Handbook. It is an hourly-average wind speed (which is different from the 3-second-average wind speed which was used in CP3) which has a probability of exceedence of 1/50 in any one year (the same as CP3). The values are lower and the isotachs more widely spaced than in CP3, the lower values are because these are hourly-average values of wind speed and not 3-second averages and the wider spacing of the isotachs is because the values presented in the present Code are values which have been 'adjusted' to sea level, and, before use, values have to be corrected for the altitude of the site. The reason for this procedure is to differentiate the Geographical and Altitude effects on the values of wind speed since the latter cannot be delineated adequately at the scale of the map.

2.2.2 | Site wind speed

The Basic Wind Speed is modified by altitude and topography (Section 2.2.2.2.), direction (Section 2.2.2.3 and Table 3), seasonal (Section 2.2.2.4 and Table D1 in Annex D), and probability (Section 2.2.2.5 and equation D1 in Annex D) factors to give the Site Wind Speed.

2.2.2.2

To make the Standard method applicable to sites with local topography, the altitude factor has been converted into an 'Altitude and Topography Factor' for the Standard method only. See the comments above on Section 1.5.1 Stages 4 and 6. Two expressions in the Standard method must be calculated, $viz.$

$$S_a = 1 + 0.001\Delta_S, \text{ or}$$
$$S_a = 1 + 0.001\Delta_T + 1.2\psi s$$

whichever is the greater must be applied, where Δ_S is the altitude of the site and Δ_T is the altitude at the base of the feature, $\psi_U = Z/L_U$, $\psi_D = Z/L_D$, where Z and L are defined in Figure 8 and s is obtained from Figures 9 or 10. The constant 1.2 assumes normal turbulence for hilly terrain and is slightly conservative. Because the philosophies behind the altitude and topography corrections are different, there will always be a discrepancy in an arbitrary boundary between the two (shown in Figure 7). There are also a few conditions when the topography 'rules' apply but the principle does not, and exclusion clauses are impossible to frame. For these reasons both values of S_a have to be calculated and the larger applied. If it is difficult to decide whether a hill (or ridge) or an escarpment (or cliff) best describes the site, then advice is given in the note at the foot of this Section.

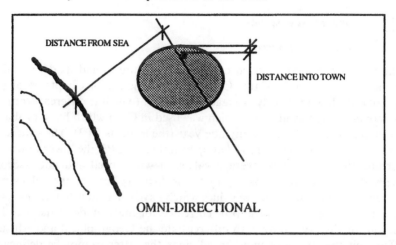

Diagram 2.5

2.2.2.3

The Directional Factor used in the Standard method needs some explanation. If no allowance is to be made, or if the orientation of the structure is unknown, then a factor of 1.0 must be used in combination with the shortest distance from the sea and the shortest distance from the edge of the town, if appropriate. If the orientation of the structure is known, because the table of pressure coefficients assume that the wind can come from any direction $\pm 45°$ and from between $180° \pm 45°$ of the stated direction, then the largest value of wind speed within those ranges should be used for a symmetric building.[2] The variation of Directional Factor with wind direction is shown on p. 73 of this Handbook with these restrictions shown, and, unless there is some other reason (such as critical distances from sea and into town, or unusual face sizes or an asymmetric building), then it is recommended in this Handbook that no account is taken of wind direction in the Standard method. This will be discussed in detail in Step 6 of Chapter 1 under 'If the Standard method is to be used for Pressure Coefficients'.

2.2.2.4

The seasonal factor is introduced either for temporary buildings which will be constructed, then taken down after use, stored and reconstructed at a future time or for the loading on buildings during construction, when some aspect of the design or construction timing renders them more susceptible to wind loading than the completed building. The object is to obtain a load which has the same probability of occurrence as the standard value of 1/50

---

[2] See the effect of a 'topography factor' in paragraph 2.2.2.2.

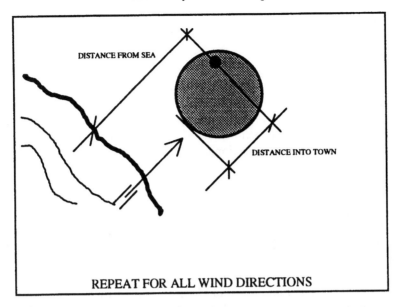

Diagram 2.6

in any one year. As winds tend to be stronger in the winter than in the summer, it can be seen in Table D1 that the wind speed which has a probability of occurring in the months of April to July inclusive is 76 per cent of the wind speed which has the same probability of occurring in the whole year. However the wind speed which has that probability of occurring in the months of December to March inclusive is the same wind speed with the identical probability of occurring during the whole year because those are the months of the year in which the extreme wind speed is most likely to occur.

2.2.2.5

Probability Factor. Because the Map Wind Speed has a probability of exceedence of 1/50 in any one year, the value of the probability factor S_p is equal to 1.0 for this probability. For other probabilities (the probability of exceedence in any one year is the reciprocal of the Return Period) the expression in Appendix F should be used. Further comments about probability are contained in Article 1 in Chapter 4 of this Handbook and the background to the 'Extreme Value Analysis' is outlined in Article 4 of Chapter 4 of this Handbook. Care must be taken if a factor other than 1.0 is used, as this may have repercussions on associated partial safety factors.

2.2.3 | *Effective wind speed*

2.2.3.1

This Section states that S_d should equal the largest value of the 'directional factor, topography factor' combination for a sector within $\pm45°$. The procedure is not as simple as this, as was explained in the discussion on Section 2.2.2.3. If a directional value of wind speed is required, then it should be obtained as explained in Section 2.2.2.3. It is always possible to use a value of S_d of 1.0 for the 'omnidirectional' case; this saves much trouble.

2.2.3.2

Because wind speed increases with height and because the reference height for Pressure Coefficients is often at the top of a building (because when pressure data from wind tunnel studies on buildings of the same plan form, but of different heights, was related to the wind speed at this height, the data collapsed to a unique set), on a very tall narrow building, the Effective Wind Speed for the whole building would be high and excessive loads would be determined. To prevent this, a rule for the division of the building into parts is detailed in this Section, in conjunction with Figure 11. Because the conservatism in CP3 has been reduced in BS 6399 by a number of measures, for instance the allowance of local shelter through the H_o term, *the new division by parts rules must be strictly obeyed* to prevent underestimation of wind loads. The value of the diagonal *'a'* used in the calculation of wind speed should be that for the combined faces and not that part under consideration.

The reason why a building which meets the requirements for 'division by parts' cannot be split into an infinite number of parts is that, due to the three dimensional nature of the flow around the building, the maximum values of pressure do not occur at the top of the building, but a distance below on the front face (and further down on the side faces). The maximum measured value of peak pressure has been converted into a value of peak pressure coefficient by dividing it by the dynamic pressure *at the top of the structure,* so the values of peak pressure coefficient are thus not academically correct pressure coefficients. The value of local peak pressure coefficient varies up the structure in a non-monotonic fashion and differently on front and side faces, so cannot be allowed for in a Code solely by the variation of dynamic pressure. By limiting the number of parts into which the building can be divided, the authors of the Code have ensured that both the maximum values of pressure are used whilst limiting the overestimation of the overall loads.

2.2.3.3

If a rectangular building with a flat roof is being considered and only two loading cases detailed, then it is essential that wind directions 180° from the axis of the calculation should also be considered as explained in the discussion on Section 2.2.2. This can be complicated by the geographic situation of the site (see Section 2.2.2.3).

2.3 | Standard pressure coefficients

2.3.1.1

Pressure is a scalar and acts in all directions. The force on a surface is equal to the product of the pressure and the area of the surface and acts *at right angles to the surface*. The *Resultant Load* in any direction can be resolved from the values of the components of load in two orthogonal directions provided the *two loads occur simultaneously*. It is the load which is resolved from the component area and not from the pressure.

2.3.1.3

This section draws the readers attention to the fact that when the load on a single face is considered, the pressure difference across that face must be calculated. This entails a calculation of the internal pressure, which is described in Section 2.6. It is usual to assume that there is a single internal pressure in a building, so that, when calculating the overall horizontal forces on a building on level ground, the internal pressure on opposite walls cancels and the overall force is calculated from the external pressure only. This also applies to overall loads in the horizontal directions on the roof, but does not apply to vertical roof loads, which are considered in Section 2.5.

2.4 | Standard external pressure coefficients for walls

The data presented here only apply to the vertical walls (less than 15° from the vertical) of rectangular buildings (for polygonal buildings see Section 2.4.2).

2.4.1 | Rectangular buildings

It is true that the dimensions B and D are 'wind dimensions' in that they change with wind direction. However, in the Standard method, this is not a problem because only two Orthogonal directions are considered, and these can be chosen to make the Wind and Body dimensions the same. If only rectangular buildings are evaluated by the Standard method, as recommended in this *Handbook*, then the values of Pressure Coefficient are given for the Front Face by

$$C_p = 0.8 - (D/H - 1.)/15.$$

and for the Rear Face by

$$C_p = -0.3 + (D/H - 1.)/15.$$

for values of D/H between 1 and 4. Outside that range of values of D/H the limiting values quoted in Table 5 apply.

2.4.1.3

The values of Pressure Coefficient are constant in zones of the Side faces, however the size of the zones varies with dimension B. Once again this is a 'Wind' dimension, but, for the two Orthogonal cases, it is equal to a 'Body' dimension, so only one calculation is required. The Scaling Length (b) can be affected by the height of the building if it is low, because, in this case, wind will prefer to flow over the building rather than round it: hence the choice of values for b.

2.4.1.4

A new concept is introduced in this paragraph; the idea of 'funnelling'. A closely adjoining building has a shielding effect on a building provided it is upwind of it. This is allowed for in paragraph 1.7.3.3. However, if the adjoining building is to the side of the building being studied, then there is a speed-up of the flow going through the gap between the buildings. This speed-up will make the local pressures more negative. The correction can be made to the load on the side faces, however, it is more important to apply it to the 'panel' load. The 'funnelled' values apply when the gap is $b/2$. The 'isolated' values apply for gaps larger than b and smaller than $b/4$. Linear interpolation between these values should be undertaken. If the Gap between the building and its neighbour is not of constant width, the value closest to $b/2$ should be used. Funnelling should be applied to all walls up to and including 15° to the vertical.

2.4.1.5

All walls within 15° of the vertical are considered to be vertical. For walls of greater inclination to the vertical, data from the Directional method (Section 3.3.1.4) should be used with the proviso of Section 2.4.2 applied. Funnelling should be applied to all walls up to and including 15° to the vertical.

2.4.2   *Polygonal buildings*

The data for pressure coefficients (Table 5) only apply to rectangular buildings. For polygonal buildings a good approximation to the loads can be obtained from the loads on the Smallest Enclosing Rectangle. If a more accurate assessment is required, especially if loads on individual faces are required, the values of pressure coefficient should be taken from Table 26 amended by the values from Table 27, both of the Directional method. It is recommended in this Handbook that the estimation of any but overall loads on 'Polygonal' buildings are obtained using the Directional method. This avoids the possible confusion and error arising from having to choose values of Pressure Coefficient which are the largest within a range of values for θ of ±45° from the angle between the ingoing normal to the face and the wind direction.

In the Standard method three or four orthogonal cases (these will be based on the directions x and y for the doubly-symmetric case, plus either $-x$ and/or $-y$ depending upon the symmetry) have to be identified and the values of Pressure Coefficient determined as the maximum values within a wind direction range of $\pm 45°$ from the orthogonal directions for every face. This takes as much time as evaluating overall loads as in the Directional method.

2.4.3   Buildings with re-entrant corners, etc.

2.4.3.1 b

The length of zone A for all but the upwind wing is calculated using the smaller of B_2 or $2H$, but zone A starts at the upwind corner of the face, i.e. on the shaded area in Figures 13(a), (b) and (c).

2.4.3.1 c

The value of D used should be for the overall building.

As with polygonal buildings, when the data from the Directional method are used in the Standard method, then maximum values within $\pm 45°$ of the orthogonal direction have to be used. Again the whole Directional method is recommended in this Handbook.

For internal wells and re-entrant bays in side faces rules are given in 2.4.3.2. It is assumed that, under heading (i) the roof, of whatever shape it is, spans the whole well.

2.4.3.2

For a bay or internal well, note the instruction that, if the bay or well spans two loading zones, then the pressure in the bay is area-averaged from the values in the different loading zones.

2.4.3.3

If the gap across well or bay is greater than the height of the building or the building is polygonal, then the Pressure Coefficient data must be obtained from the Directional method (3.3.1.7), otherwise Pressure Coefficient data from either method can be used.

2.4.4   Buildings with irregular or inset faces

2.4.4.1   Irregular flush faces

Data are presented in Tables 5 or 26 and 27, and descriptions in Figures 14 and 15. It is assumed that, if the front and rear faces are flush, then the pressure on the front and rear faces of the buildings are given in Table 5. For the front face the value of D should be that for the part adjoining the face and for the rear face should be the whole length of the building. For example, in Figure 14a the value of D for the front face would be the length of the tall part and for the rear face of the raised storey would be the length of the raised storey, but for the rear face of the lower part would be the value for the whole building. For Figure 14b the value of D for the front face of the lower storey would be the length of the lower storey and for the upper storey would be the length of the upper storey, and the value of D for the rear faces would be the whole length.

The pressure on the side faces is given in Table 5 with the zone sizes dependent upon b, which depends upon either H or B, the latter being defined in this Section as the *cross-wind breadth of a windward face*. For Figures 14b and 14d lower and upper parts are carefully defined in the text.

2.4.4.2 *Walls on inset storeys*

Procedure for the calculation of pressures on side faces is given in this Section. The value of pressure coefficient in zone E (defined in Figure 15b) is given in the text as -2.0. This region of high suction is caused by the presence of a small vortex in this region.

The pressure on front and rear walls should be taken from Table 5 in the cases of both Figure 15a and Figure 15b.

2.4.6 *Circular plan buildings*

Data are presented in Table 7 and linear interpolation for values of H/d between 2.5 and 10 is allowed. For values of H/d less than 2.5, the values for $H/d = 2.5$ should be used. Similarly for values of H/d greater than 10, the values for $H/d = 10$ should be used. The variation of values with H/d on Table 7 is to allow for end effects on separation. The length effects are allowed for in Figure 25.

A circular, or any non sharp-edged building presents difficulties to the wind engineer. The problem arises because the point of separation of the air flow around the building is ill-defined and varies depending upon the turbulence and speed of the approaching wind, the roughness of the surface and the Aspect Ratio (ratio of length to width) of the building. This is explained at length in Article 2 of Chapter 4 of this Handbook as the reason why the restriction to a minimum diameter of 1 m must be observed.

The region around $\theta = 40°$ is where the pressure changes from positive to negative. This zero pressure point moves continually on the surface, due to turbulence, and, as the slope of the pressure/incidence curve is large at this angular location, the pressure varies rapidly between large limits at this point for relatively small changes of wind direction due to turbulence.

If data from a source other than the Code are used for the values of Pressure Coefficient, they should be examined very carefully before use to ensure that they are in the same format and relative to the same reference as the rest of the data in this Code.

Designers of circular structures would be well advised to seek specialist advice.

2.5 | External Pressure Coefficients on roofs

2.5.1 | *Flat roofs*

Roofs with a pitch angle less than 5° are defined as flat.

The scaling length for flat roofs is given in Section 2.5.1.2 (Figure 16 applies) and for mono- and duopitch roofs in Section 2.5.2 (Figures 19 and 20 apply). Note that the height of the building used for the calculation of the scaling length is the height of the wall *including the parapet* if present.

2.5.1.4

The loading on the parapet walls themselves is calculated from the data of Table 21 (see Section 2.7.5) and not from data for the walls. There should be the one loading case for the front parapet wall, and components of this load should be added to the two orthogonal cases. Note that values of pressure for parapets from Table 21 are values of *pressure difference across the parapet* whereas the values of pressure on the walls are values of external pressure and have to be combined with values of internal pressure to obtain values of pressure difference across the wall. Thus there appears to be a discontinuity of loading on the front face of the building, which does not, in fact, exist. As regards the loading on the whole building, if the inwind depth (D) of the building is greater than H, the loading on the parapet on the rear wall should be the same as a parapet with return corners in Table 21. The reason is because it has been assumed that the flow has re-attached to the roof before the parapet on the rear wall. If the windwise distance (D) is less than H, the rear parapet can be considered to be an extension of the rear wall.

2.5.1.5

Flat roofs with curved eaves. The wall is assumed to finish at the start of the curved portion. For the region between this and the flat portion of the roof see section 2.5.1.5.2.

2.5.1.7

In this Section on flat roofs with inset stories, note that different values of H are used: H_r to determine the reference height (the height at which wind speeds are calculated) and H the height of the inset storey to determine the scaling length (which can determine the size of the loading zones). Values of pressure coefficient should be taken from Table 8, except for those areas where they are defined by the walls.

2.5.2

For monopitch and duopitch roofs (see Figures 19 and 20) in Figure 19b zones A and B are always at the windward eave. For instance, for wind direction 0° (see Figure 19a) zones A and B are the low eave and for wind direction 180° they are the high eave. Note also that the scaling length is based on either L, W or H; all of which are *Body Dimensions* and do not change with wind direction.

The instructions for interpolation in Tables 9 to 11 are for interpolation between values of pressure coefficient of the same sign. Thus, for example, in Table 9 zone A for $\theta = 0°$, interpolation for α of 5°, 15° and 30° would be for values -1.7, -0.9 and -0.5: and for α of 15°, 30° and 45° would be $+0.2$, $+0.5$ and $+0.7$ respectively. At any value in this range both a positive and a negative number should be calculated and the value which gives the highest overall load should be retained.

In Tables 10 and 11 for pitch angles of 15° and 30°, two values are given for zones A to C. The advice given earlier does not necessarily apply in this case. The values for zones E to J are all negative, so that the choice of negative values for zones A to C will give the largest vertical load on the roof. However, the choice of the positive values could give a greater load in the horizontal direction. Thus both loads must be calculated and the greater horizontal roof load should be added to the horizontal wall loads.

2.5.2.4.2

For values of $\alpha < 7°$ and $W < b_L$, it is assumed that the separation region from the front eave covers not only the upwind roof, but extends onto the downwind roof. This then tends to the situation described for the flat roof as shown in Figure 16.

2.5.4   *Mansard roofs*

The data from Tables 10 and 11 apply. Figure 22 should be studied.

2.5.5   *Multi-bay roofs*

In multi-bay roofs, the width W is taken as the width of a single bay (see the right-hand side of Figures 19c or 20c). In Section 2.5.5 (b), and Figure 23c , the 'treat as monopitch' applies to the upwind bay and the first duopitch is treated as the second bay in Figure 23d. In multi-bay ridged duopitch roofs, treat the whole of the first bay as a duopitch and treat the upwind faces of second and subsequent bays as downwind faces of a troughed duopitch, and the downwind faces of second and subsequent bays as the downwind face of a ridged duopitch. This contradicts the instruction in the Code.

2.5.8

The value of the scaling length used for the calculation of Small Overhangs should be the value for the roof (either b_L or b_W) for the upper surface and the value of b from Section 2.4.1.3 for the undersurface from wall data.

2.5.9.1.2

The 'Reference Height' for canopies is shown in Figure 24 to be the highest point of the roof. The Reference Height for canopy data in item 6 in the references is the mid-height of the roof and data from that source should use its own reference height.

2.5.9.1.5

The 'reference height' for the values of Pressure Coefficient quoted in this Section should be the highest point of the canopy which is the Reference Height for the canopy.

2.5.10

Zones D and J are regions of attached flow and that is the reason why frictional loads act here and not elsewhere. The direction of friction loads is in the direction of the wind in the plane of the surface.

2.6   Standard internal Pressure Coefficients

The expression for the diagonal 'a' for internal pressures is an empirical expression. The actual limiting averaging time for the fluctuations of pressure within a building depends upon the size and shape of the openings, the internal volume and the pressure difference between the inside and the outside of the building. This could then be converted into an effective diagonal 'a' size, but the expression is cumbersome. The expression given in this Section gives a conservative estimate of the most probable value. To be clear, there are three expressions for the diagonal 'a' for internal volumes:

$$a = 10 \times \sqrt[3]{(internal\ volume)}\text{ for a sealed building,}$$

$$a = 0.2 \times \sqrt[3]{(internal\ volume)}\text{ for a building with a dominant opening, or}$$

$$a = \text{diagonal dimension of the dominant opening.}$$

In the case of the dominant opening the *larger* of the latter two values is used. The values of $C_{pi} = -0.3$ or $+0.2$ apply if there is no dominant opening, the one which gives the larger load across the surface being chosen. In the case of a dominant opening, the relation of the value of the Internal Pressure Coefficient to the value of the External Pressure Coefficient at the opening is given in Table 17.

   The Reference Height for the calculation of internal pressure ought to be the highest point on the wall of the building in which the opening occurs. However, in the case where division-by-parts is undertaken and the internal volume of the storey or room and not the building is used, then the same rules apply as for the determination of the external pressure (see Section 2.2.3.2).

2.6.4

The diagonal *'a'* is the diameter of the open topped cylinder, and the Reference Height is the top of the structure.

| 2.7 | Pressure coefficients on elements

The choice of a maximum diameter of 200 mm for circular elements is to restrict the flow regime to the subcritical, i.e. where the flow in the boundary layer is laminar and flow separation occurs early, producing a wide wake and high drag. For larger sizes the value of the Pressure Coefficient will be smaller, but, as its value depends upon the turbulence of the approaching airstream, the surface roughness of the cylinder and the wind speed, it is not possible to be more specific in a Code. The values of Table 7 refer to cylinders whose diameter is greater than 1 m and the flow in the boundary layer is turbulent, the wake is narrower and the drag is lower than the value given in Table 20.

The presence of an element on the surface of a body however, can cause changes of a considerable magnitude to the loads on the host body, especially on a circular body. The whole question of this interaction should be considered seriously, and, if in doubt, advice should be sought.

2.7.4

The loading of clad buildings in their unclad state during construction ought to be seriously considered. This is mentioned in the note in Section 1.5.2. Not only should the effect of the missing cladding be considered, but also the stability of the frames themselves.

In all but the most simple cases, BS 8100 should be used for the design of lattice towers and masts.

2.7.5.4

The value of *'h'* used here ought to be the value for the upwind fence. It says in Section 2.7.5.2 that the wind direction for maximum loading either at a return end, or at the end of the wall is at 45° to the wall. However, away from the end, the maximum load will be for a wind normal to the fence. The values in Table 21 occur for different wind directions and are the largest value in their zone. The spacing (X) in Figure 27 is normal to the fence.

Section 3. Directional method

General comments

This method is called the 'directional method' because the loads are calculated for a number of specific wind directions, usually 12. It can take advantage of the fact that the effective wind speeds, upon which the loads are based, vary with direction, and, if a building is so oriented that its largest side faces into the weakest winds, then the design loads are less than they would be if the largest side faced into the strongest winds. The method also covers a vastly increased range of planforms of building shapes for which no data are available in the Standard method.

3.1.1

Wind direction is always defined as the direction from which the wind has come and is measured in degrees east of north, sometimes abbreviated to EON. Thus 90° EON is a wind blowing from the east. Wind data are always based upon this direction, and it is represented by ϕ.

The pressure coefficient data are all presented relative to a wind direction θ, which is the angle between the ingoing normal to the face and the wind direction. Values of θ vary from 0° to 180°. There is no difference in the values of pressure coefficient for positive or negative values of θ.

Do not confuse these two angles.

3.1.2   Dynamic pressure

Note in equation 16 that V_e is always the Effective Wind Speed, but that q, the value of dynamic pressure has no subscript. The reason is that, in the Directional method, the 'size factor' appears in the value of wind speed and therefore also in the value of dynamic pressure. This means that the value of V_e used for the calculation of external pressure will be different from the value of V_e used for the calculation of internal pressure. This is why you are asked to calculate the various values of dynamic pressure at this stage. Hereafter values of wind speed will not be mentioned.

3.1.3.1   Directional surface pressures

This Section describes the evaluation of pressures from pressure coefficients and dynamic pressures, the latter value depends whether option (iv) (the full Directional method) or option (v) (the Handbook Best Buy) is used. Take care to use C_a on the dynamic pressure and not on the wind speed if option (v) is used (see pp.7 and 8 of this Handbook).

3.1.3.2   Directional surface loads

Note that the Dynamic Augmentation Factor does not apply to individual faces.

3.1.3.3   Directional overall loads

These are calculated from a new expression of which that used in the Standard method is a limiting case. It assumes that the pressure coefficient on all faces facing upwind (called 'front') is equal to $C_{pf} \cos \theta$, where θ is the angle between the wind and the normal to the face: and the pressure coefficient on all rear facing faces (downwind) is equal to C_{pr}, where C_{pf} and C_{pr} are the values given in Table 5, interpolated for the value of D/H. The expression gives the force in the wind direction. This is explained in paragraph 3.1.3.3.2. The multiplier 0.85 is to allow for the fact that the peak gusts do not occur simultaneously on opposite faces. Note that 'W' is the smaller of the faces of the enclosing rectangle (see Figure 30). There is no funnelling considered in the calculation of overall loads in the Directional method: this is because values of external pressure coefficient for front and rear faces are considered and these contain no correction for funnelling.

3.1.3.4   Directional frictional drag component

This states that the frictional force calculated on long walls 'should be taken to act in the wind direction'. This is not correct because frictional forces act along the surface, and this is not the same thing. Hopefully the discrepancy is small.

3.1.3.5   Directional cladding (panel) loads

This is where the Code gives permission formally for option (v) to be applied to panels. When applying option (v) to panels, correct the panel wind speed for the actual panel size from that for the 'minimal face'. The 'correction' of this value to the size of panel under consideration is achieved by the use of the 'size effect factor' (C_a) of the Standard method. (Note that the value for C_a for a 5 m panel is 1.0, and is equivalent to a value of wind speed in the Directional method using a value of 3.44 for g_t).

3.1.3.5.2

This explains that the correction for diagonal 'a' using C_a is made to the value of dynamic pressure $(1/2\rho V^2)$ and not to V.

3.2   Directional wind speeds
3.2.1

The basic wind speed comes from the map and is therefore geography dependent only.

3.2.2

The site wind speed is direction dependent through the directional and topographical corrections. There will therefore be a 'site wind speed' for every direction studied.

If topography is significant then the value for S_a is controlled by the height of the base of the topographical feature. As with the Standard method, the greater of the values of S_a (using topography or not) should be chosen. In the indeterminate case, described in paragraph 5.2.2.6, the same advice should be followed. See paragraph 3.2.3.4 for a full comment on the topography factor.

3.2.3

The effective wind speed is size and height dependent as well as direction dependent, so that a different value must be calculated for every combination of wind direction, height (if division by parts is used) and size of item (different values for cladding, faces and overall loads).

3.2.3.1

Note that the term S_b is a function of *Effective* Height. This is the 'building-by parts' paragraph and the comments on Section 2.2.3.2 and Figure 11 should be studied carefully. *It is important that the rules are applied accurately*, the reasons are given in the commentary to Section 2.2.3.2.

3.2.3.2.1 d

Under option (v) three values of Dynamic Pressure have to be calculated for every wind direction at every Effective Height; this requirement arises out of the different areas over which correlation of the gusts is required. The first value is that from which the load on a panel or part of a face of the building is calculated, and usually has a diagonal size '*a*' of 5 m. The second is that from which the internal pressure is calculated and the expression for the diagonal '*a*' is given in Section 2.6. This second value is required because the openings between the inside and outside of the building, coupled with the internal volume of the building, filter out the high frequency content of the pressure fluctuations produced by the turbulence of the wind. The third value is that from which the load on the overall building and the faces thereof are calculated, and is based upon the diagonal '*a*' for the Maximal Face (see Section 3.1.3.2 and Figure 5b). This is allowed in Section 3.2.3.3.3.

3.2.3.2

These are the corrections which convert the hourly-average wind speed for the site into a gust wind speed at an Effective Height. The corrections relate to the roughness of the ground. As the wind blows over a long stretch of sea, it develops a velocity profile (variation of speed with height) and a turbulence profile (variation of turbulence with height) appropriate to the roughness of the sea. As soon as the wind reaches land, the ground roughness under the wind changes and the layers of wind close to the surface adapt to their new roughness, the effect spreading higher into the atmosphere with the length of land. If the land extended sufficiently far, all memory of the sea profile would be lost. When a town is reached, the rougher surface of the town creates more turbulence, which gradually with distance, spreads to higher layers of the atmosphere. When the town is passed, then the 'country' roughness begins again at the lowest layers and gradually the effect of the town is lost. A fuller description is given in Article 2.

3.2.3.2.1

Shear Forces and Bending Moments on the whole building should be based upon the diagonal 'a' of the Combined Faces (defined on p. 11), and have the 0.85 factor for non-correlation across faces applied (if the 0.85 factor has already been used in the calculation of the loads, then it must not be applied again here). Shear Force and Bending Moments of the building about a height ought to be based on the diagonal 'a' of the Combined Faces of the loaded part of the building above the height in question and have the 0.85 factor applied once if it has not been applied in the calculation of the loads.

3.2.3.3 | Gust peak factor

This is where the diagonal 'a' size is allowed for in the Directional method. This follows an academically correct procedure.

3.2.3.3.1

This Section states that the dynamic pressure used on any surface must be calculated for a diagonal 'a' of that surface; this is the Option (iv) approach and can involve a great deal of work. It is recommended in this Handbook that option (v) is used.

3.2.3.3.2

Here it states clearly that the value used for H_r is the value at the top of the building. However in paragraph 3.2.3.1 explaining the 'division by parts' rule, the value used for H_r is the height of the top *of that part*. It is recommended here that this relaxation is used.

3.2.3.3.3

This is where the use of C_a is allowed, see Section 3.1.3.5.1.

3.2.3.3.4

See notes on Section 3.1.3.1.2.

3.2.3.4 | Topography factor

The definition of 'significant zones' for topography are shown in Figure 7. Because the philosophies behind the altitude and topography corrections are different, there will always be a discrepancy in an arbitrary boundary between the two. For this reason two conditions need to be considered:

(i)   an altitude correction for the altitude of the site;

(ii)   an altitude correction for the altitude of the base of the hill, and a topography factor for the effect of the hill.

The larger resulting wind speed should be applied. This is considered further in Section 3.2.3.4.10.

3.2.3.4.5

For multiple hills, etc., the procedures of this Code only apply to the hill on which the site is located, the other hills are taken into account by the altitude correction; the altitude factor *for the foot of the hill on which the site stands* must be used. The presence of the upwind hills does increase the turbulence of the wind slightly, but this can be ignored. See also 3.2.3.4.7.

3.2.3.4.7

Note that the value for the slope is the ratio Z/L and is not the angle but the tangent of the angle. Take care with the logarithmic scale for H/L in Figures 9 and 10 and the different values for L in different parts of Figure 8. Advice on the value of Δ_T is given in this paragraph.

3.2.3.4.9

If there is difficulty in differentiating between hills (and ridges) and cliffs (and escarpments), this paragraph should be studied.

3.2.3.4.10

Figure 7 shows the areas where the topography can be considered 'significant'. The altitude factor and the topography factor allow for much the same fact, the height of the site. The difference is the steepness of the local terrain, and the mechanism which causes the change of wind speed is different in the two cases. When an arbitrary line is drawn between the two effects, there will almost always be a discontinuity in the numerical values calculated by the two methods. With somewhat crude rules, it is inevitable that there will be cases which come under one set of rules but the other mechanism applies; this is unfortunate. In the Standard method there is a requirement that both altitude and topography should be considered and the one giving the larger loads used. This was simple as the choice was between the numbers from two simple expressions. In the Directional method, the requirement to use whichever gives the higher load still applies, but the calculation is more complex because the Altitude correction is applied in converting the Map Wind Speed to the Site Wind Speed and the Topography correction is applied in the conversion from the Site Wind Speed to the Effective Wind Speed. The rest of the factors stay the same, but the calculation is longer.

3.2.3.4.11

When Z/L is greater than 0.3 for the downwind slope, the flow is separated from the hill. This can sometimes be accompanied by fast winds a little distance above the ground, with very little wind at ground level. If this situation would materially affect your design, then specialist advice should be sought.

3.3 | Directional pressure Coefficients

3.3.1 | External pressure coefficients for walls

3.3.1.1.2

Dimensions B and D are *Wind Dimensions* and are different for each wind direction. However, as this Section refers to rectangular planform buildings the values of B and D are given by

$$B = W \times abs\ (\sin[\theta]) + L \times abs\ (\cos[\theta])$$

$$D = W \times abs\ (\sec[\theta])\ \text{or}\ D = L \times abs\ (\cos\ ec[\theta])$$

whichever is smaller.

In Table 26, (see Figure 31), linear interpolation should be undertaken for intermediate values of D/H. Linear interpolation is not sufficiently accurate for intermediate values of wind direction; this should either be done graphically or by computer using spline/splint techniques. In zones A and D values of pressure coefficient of ± 0.2 are given. The choice should be to produce the largest load on the wall. This will usually be achieved by choosing the same sign as the values in the other zones of the wall. However the maximum overall load on a building is achieved by using the maximum value on all sides whose component of area faces one way and the minimum on sides whose component of area faces in the opposite direction, so that the max-

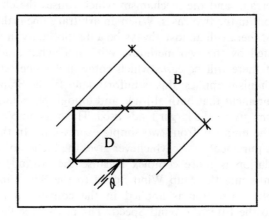

Diagram 2.7

imum overall load does not necessarily come from integrating the components of the maximum loads on individual faces.

3.3.1.1.3

This paragraph refers to the interaction of one building on its close neighbour called 'funnelling' and assumes that the gap between the two buildings is constant. This subject is complex, and, if in doubt, for example if the two buildings are not parallel and the gap varies, then the gap nearest to $b/2$ should be used. Note that, although the maximum correction on values of External Pressure Coefficient is 20 per cent, the correction on panel loads can be more than this if values of Internal Pressure Coefficient are negative. Note that the Directional method for the calculation of Overall loads does not allow for 'funnelling'. This can be allowed for by adding components of face loads with the 0.85 factor included.

3.3.1.2.1

This paragraph gives permission for a slight reduction in the work load at the expense of a slight increase in load on vertical walls (a similar reduction for roofs is allowed in Section 3.3.2.2.2) if desired. The cross-wind breadth B is a 'wind dimension' in that it changes with wind direction. The sizes of the zones on walls varies as the scaling length 'b' which depends either on B or H. This means that it has to be calculated afresh for every wind direction. For a building of complex planform, this can involve considerable work. In the paragraph permission is given to use the minimum enclosing rectangle (or circle), which reduces the work considerably, thus (see sketch in Section 3.3.1.1.2):

$$B = W \times abs\ (\sin[\theta]) + L \times abs\ (\cos[\theta])$$

$$D = W \times abs\ (\sec[\theta])\ \text{or}\ L \times abs\ (\cos\ ec[\theta])$$

whichever is smaller, and L and W are the length and width of the minimum enclosing rectangle. If an enclosing circle gives a better fit, then $B = D = diameter$. However, in the procedure described in 'Steps useful for frequent users' in Chapter 1 of this Handbook, the derivation of the correct value of B causes little additional trouble. In a completely computer-oriented solution, this simplification could be useful.

3.3.1.2.2

This states by default that if the width of zone A is not its full width of $b/5$, then *no* reduction is allowable in Table 27. In this Table, if the value of β is less than 60°, the value for 60° shall be used, and if the value of β is greater than 150°, then the value for 150° shall be used.

_3.3.1.2.3_

This is to ensure that nowhere on a wall is there a negative pressure greater than the value at the corner.

_3.3.1.3_

The Reference Height for the vertical wall below the gable zones shown in Table 28 should be that shown on Figure 33.

_3.3.1.3.3_

The same advice on the close proximity of buildings as given in the comments on Section 3.3.1.1.3 apply.

_3.3.1.4_ *Non-vertical walls*

When using wall data, the values of *B* and *D* should be calculated for every wind direction and should be based upon ground level dimensions and the circumscribing rectangular or circle can be used.

_3.3.1.5_

A single minimum enclosing rectangle is impossible to define in this case and reference should be made to the sketches below. The text requires that the 'upwind wing' be treated differently for some wind directions, this same difference must be made to the minimum enclosing rectangle. Two minimum enclosing rectangles are therefore defined in Section 3.3.1.5.a, one for the Upwind Wing and the other for the rest of the building. Neither the Upwind Wing nor the Smallest Enclosed Rectangle change with wind direction, but the values of *B* and *D* do. An Upwind Wing of

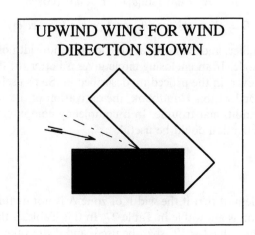

UPWIND WING FOR WIND DIRECTION SHOWN

Diagram 2.8

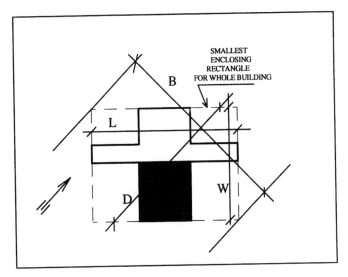

Diagram 2.9

this kind of building is shown in Figure 33. It is so-called because the approaching wind meets the front face of this wing as if this wing were the only building present. Consequently the sizes of the zones on the front face and at the start of the side faces are defined by the scaling length related either to H or the cross-wind dimension *of the wing alone*. This is shown in the sketch. The value of $\pm45°$ as the limits for so treating the wing is approximate and is reasonable when the re-entrant corner is $90°$, it might be better to consider the limit to be half the adjoining re-entrant angle when the corner is not $90°$; this is also shown in the sketch. For the whole building, the values of B and D should be determined from the minimum enclosing rectangle for the whole building (and will vary with wind direction). For the 'upwind wing', the values of B and D shall be determined relative to the minimum enclosing rectangle *for the wing* and β should be the angle between the wind direction and the ingoing normal to the face in question. For different wind directions, different parts of the building will become the 'upwind wing'.

The zone D is that at the rear of a wall, and the pressure there represents the speed-up as the wind expands behind the wall. It is therefore correct for there to be no zone D where the wall terminates in a re-entrant corner. Likewise zones A and B represent the regions of high suction at the front edge of the wall; where the wall starts at a re-entrant corner, it is correct for there to be no zones A and B. If there is any doubt which zones apply, the instructions in this section are explicit.

The line defining the 'wedge' is normal to the wind direction and its size is clearly defined in Figure 33. The length of the wedge is equal to 'b', where 'b' is the scaling length for the rest of the building. The pressure coefficient for parts of the walls within the wedge are given in 3.3.1.5.2 to be that for $\theta = 0°$ from Table 33, the values used for B and D should be the value for the rest of the building. See also comments on Section 3.3.1.6.1.c.

3.3.1.6 | Buildings with recessed bays

For buildings with recessed bays, the minimum enclosing rectangle shall be used for the derivation of B and D.

3.3.1.6.1.b

For the narrow recess ($G < b/2$), the value in zone A of the recessed wall (see Figure 34a) is the value for the A zones on the face in which the recess is located. It is calculated from the wind direction θ for the face in which the recess is located and not from the value of θ for the recessed wall. The pressure at all points marked A in Figure 34a is the same. The value of b is based on the whole building.

3.3.1.6.1.c

For the wide recess ($G > b/2$), the value for w should be equal or less than b. This means that, if G is just larger than $b/2$, then the wedge starts at the outside corner. It has been assumed that inset faces which face upwind experience the same pressures (without the zone D, which never occurs on inset faces because it represents the acceleration of the flow as it leaves the trailing edge of the building) as the front faces. For $G = b/2$, this is a conservative approximation which becomes progressively more realistic as G increases. Loading zones are defined by the rules in Section 3.3.1.5. See example on p. 109.

3.3.1.7.2.a

If the well should span two loading zones, then the value of the pressure in the well should be uniform and be the area-weighted average value over the area of the roof removed to form the well.

3.3.1.7.2.b

The remarks about Section 3.3.1.6.1.b. apply.

3.3.1.8

The remarks about Section 2.4 apply to the Directional method as far as procedure is concerned, the data are taken from Directional method tables.

3.3.1.9

Frictional loads should be applied when zones C and D occur, i.e. when $D > b$. This is because the flow is attached to the surface in these zones. In zones A and B the flow is separated and can apply no frictional load to the surface.

3.3.2 | External pressure coefficients for flat roofs

3.3.2.1.2

The simpler method for roofs on rectangular buildings saves so much time that it is recommended by this Handbook. This is repeated in Sections 3.3.3.3.3 and 3.3.3.4.3. The great saving in time in this procedure over that of the general method arises because the scaling lengths are based on body dimensions.

3.3.2.2.2

The values of B and D can be determined from the circumscribing rectangle with the expressions given in the comments to Section 3.3.1.2.1. This means that Figure 30a applies and the Minimum Enclosing Rectangle is used; note that values of B and D change with Wind Direction.

3.3.2.2.3

This is the general method and should be used for buildings of non-rectangular planform. Figure 35 shows the loading on one part of the roof only. Note that, for the wind direction shown, the part of the roof at the right hand end, which has an eave line parallel to that being considered is treated as integral with that part of the roof. Figure 36 shows zones allocated to all parts of the roof and should be studied if any doubt arises about the allocation of roof zones.

3.3.2.4.2

Figure 17a shows a parapet and its relation to the roof. The parapet is designed from the strength standpoint when it is at the front of the roof. The fact that it will experience lower loads when it is on a rear face is not considered. If only one calculation of the load on a parapet is made, it ought to be for the face which experiences the highest wind speeds, i.e. closest to 240° EON in most instances in the UK. In the unusual instance of a parapet which is stronger for inward loads than outward loads (or vice-versa), then both calculations should be made and the critical one used.

3.3.2.5

Figure 17b shows the curved eave in relation to the rest of the roof: note where the roof zones commence. The interpolation of the values for the external pressure around the curved part of a curved eave should be a linear variation with angle between the value at the top of the wall and the value at the start of zone A on the roof where the roof is again flat. The zones on roof and wall do not correspond so this will introduce inconsistencies, which should be minimized by ensuring that the differences used are of the same order as the instantaneous difference between the values in adjacent zones.

3.3.2.6

Figure 17c shows the start of the roof zones for a Mansard roof. The wall is designed using wall data. The intervening sloped part is designed using the data of Table 33, Figure 22 showing the zones. The scaling length can depend on the value of B for the minimum enclosing rectangle.

3.3.2.7

In addition to the rules in Sections 3.3.2.7.a and b, which are specific for most cases, the following instruction should be followed. In the case of a parapet on the roof, the reference height (H_r) should be taken to the top of the parapet. The same value of D based on the Minimum Enclosing Rectangle should be used in the determination of the pressure in zones X and Y as was used in the determination of the wall pressures because the assumption here is that the same pressure applies to both roof and wall in the junction region. Note that Figure 37 is a true plan.

3.3.3 | External Pressure on Pitched Roofs

3.3.3

Notice that all 'plan' drawings in Figures 38, 39 and 40 are true plans, the dimensions are in the horizontal x, y plane. *They are not dimensions in the plane of the roof surface.*

3.3.3.1

Wherever possible steep-pitched surfaces attached to vertical walls should be interpreted as 'pitched roofs' because the work involved is much less.

3.3.3.2.2

Note that the 'reference height' on Figure 38 is the height of the *higher* eave so that the height for which the effective wind speed is calculated does not change with wind direction.

3.3.3.3.3

Because the scaling length is defined in body dimensions, the zones do not change for every wind direction, in fact there are only four alternatives, and even then the sizes are the same. The four possible alternatives are shown in Figure 39. There are special cases when the situation moves from one arrangement to another, the cases of $\theta = 0°$ and $90°$. For the flow normal to the verge ($\theta = 90°$), the two left-hand schemes will give the same load on the roof, but, as the edge zones A to D are at different heights from the ground, the overturning moments will be different and both cases should be considered. The changeover from left-hand to right-hand schemes will give identical results and only one need be examined.

3.3.3.4.3

This concerns flat or almost flat duopitch roofs and considers the situation when the roof is narrow enough for the separation from the front edge to encompass the ridge line, so that the whole of the front faces, the ridge line and part of the rear roof are in separated flow. Reattachment depends upon many parameters and cannot be defined exactly, so, for this situation, the designer has to perform two calculations, one for separated flow and the other for reattached flow and then consider the loading appropriate to the higher loading. There is no suggestion that the sizes of the zones should change with B, only that the additional cases should be studied in this condition.

3.3.3.5 | *Hipped roofs*

Note that the 'plan' on Figure 41b is a true plan and that dimensions b_L and b_W are measurements in the horizontal x, y plane. Notice also that the extra zones U to Y do not occur for negative values of the pitch angle, when these zones would be in regions of separated flow.

3.3.3.7.1

The second sentence would be clearer if written 'Owing to the way that parapets around roofs change to negative pressure the positive pressures expected on upwind pitches with large positive pitch angles, neglecting their effect is not always conservative'. The Reference Height is always the highest point on the roof.

3.3.3.8 | *Pitched roofs with inset stories*

The zones X and Y should be considered the same size as for flat roofs.

3.3.4 | **Multipitch and multi-bay roofs**

3.3.4.1.2

The Reference Height should be taken as the height of the highest point of the roof.

3.3.4.2

The Reference Height for multi-bay roofs is the height of the highest point of the roof. This procedure can produce questionable results.

3.3.5 | **Internal Pressure Coefficients**

The Directional procedure has nothing to add to the Standard method in the matter of internal pressures except in the case of open sided buildings, when the value of internal pressure is dependent on wind direction. The data in Table 18 in the Standard method only have values for every 90° of wind direction, additional data for the Directional method are given in Table 37. Otherwise the same procedures as for the Standard method should be followed.

3.4   Hybrid ombinations

These have been discussed at length in the pick-and-mix sections in Chapter 1 and the remarks made then should have been noted.

Annex A. Necessary provisions for wind tunnel testing

A1 Static structures

Anyone considering placing a contract with a laboratory to conduct a wind tunnel investigation should ensure that the laboratory conducting the investigation does so according to the rules laid down in this Annex. This applies even if the wind tunnel investigation is to measure environmental wind conditions, or the emissions from chimneys or any other set of measurements which have no application to wind loading.

A2 Dynamic structures

Serious consideration should be given to the case of Dynamic Structures. A fully dynamic wind tunnel model is extremely expensive, and the investigation is extremely difficult to perform and is therefore grossly expensive. However, it is the case with most dynamic structures that the aerodynamics of the flow around the structure is unaffected by the movement of the structure. It is then possible to conduct a wind tunnel investigation on a rigid model and obtain the aerodynamic derivatives therefrom and to apply them to a mathematical model of the structure in a computer. This technique can, in the cases to which it applies, give better data than a fully dynamic investigation.

There is also a half-way house procedure which can be employed in those cases when the movement of the structure might be deemed to have a small effect and this is to use a 'semi-rigid' model. In this the practice of the aeronautical profession is followed. The technique is to calculate the fundamental frequency of oscillation of the structure and to construct a rigid wind tunnel model but mount it on a spring which has the scaled fundamental frequency.[3] This cuts down the cost of the model very considerably and can make a more useful model. A pressure tapped model may also be necessary to obtain all the data required.

ulation of the scaling frequency is given in T.V. Lawson *Wind Effects on Buildings* ablished by Allied Science Publishers, 1980.

A dynamic investigation should never be started without a full discussion with the wind tunnel laboratory at which it is expected to carry out the work. Expert advice is essential.

Annex B. Derivation of Extreme Wind Information

This topic has been discussed in Article 1 in Chapter 4 on the derivation of Meteorological Data and in Article 4 on Statistics. Either or both of these articles will give more background to this topic than is contained in this Annex.

Annex D. Probability Factor and Seasonal Factor

Background information on the general subject matter of this Annex is given in the article on Statistics.

Annex F. Gust peak factor

This explains how the 'gust peak factor' in the Directional method, which is derived by integration of the Spectrum of Turbulence (see Article 4 in Chapter 4 on Statistics) is related to the averaging time. It also introduces the TVL formula which relates the minimum averaging time of a gust which will have a contribution to the maximum loading on a panel of given size. The two concepts are combined in the Gust Peak Factor which is the centre-piece of the derivation of wind speeds in the Directional method.

The size factor of the simplified method, which is recommended for use at times in the Directional method as option (v), is derived empirically to approximate to the envelope of values calculated by the Directional method.

List of references

These have been referred to in the text.

Index to the Code

In the following Index, the terms with the prefix 2 refer to the Standard and those with the prefix 3 to the Directional method.

3

Examples

In Diagram 3.1 (p. 73) three plots of the Directional factor are presented. The first line is that for the Directional method. The second is that for the Standard method, assuming that the value is greatest within a direction range of $\pm 45°$ of the stated wind direction. The third is for a rectangular building and the value is greatest for $\pm 45° \pm 180°$. It will be seen that the advantage of the third curve is practically nil and not worth the effort.

Examples and specimen calculations are presented in the following pages in three groups:

- The first group are calculations of Effective Wind Speeds by both the Directional and Standard methods. The purpose of these is twofold: firstly to show the differences in the values obtained by the two methods which will assist in the choice of method to be used. Secondly they can be used as calibrations for any computer program written by the user.
- The second group are estimates of Pressure Coefficients for a series of different cases which can be calculated by either method to assist the user in deciding which method to use in the evaluation of pressure coefficients.
- The third group are examples of loading calculations with different purposes.

At the start of each group there is a list of definitions for all the symbols used in that group.

Throughout all the examples which follow, when pressure coefficients are converted into loads (Group 2 Sections 2, 3 and 4) the fairly strongly distorted (by direction) wind pattern of a Large Coastal Town with the Site very close to the sea have been used. This is to emphasize the differences which orientation can make. This 'reference' situation is shown in the top illustration on p. 91. The height of the buildings for most examples is 20 m, although this does change and has to be taken into account in the values of wind speed used. However, the diagonal 'a' does change from example to example and the values of VO used in the examples are the correct values for the example and not those presented on p. 91. The same 'Standard Distorted Topography' is used for the wind speeds on pp. 96 and 97.

DIRECTIONAL FACTOR

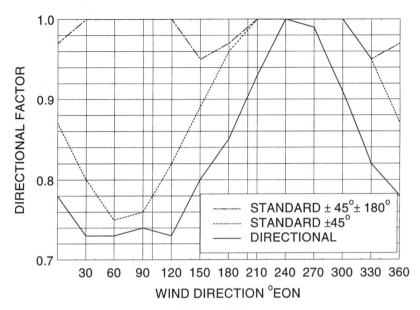

Diagram 3.1

Group 1. Section 1. Wind speed calculations

In this first section (pp. 74–82), comparisons are made between the values for the Standard and Directional methods.

Each block of numbers represents values of Wind Speed for a given value of Distance from the Sea (DS).

The rows of data are as follows:

DS   is the distance from the sea in km.

DT   is the distance within a town in km.

S005   is the value of wind speed, calculated by the Standard method for a panel of diagonal size 5 m.

D005   is the value of wind speed, calculated by the Directional method for a panel of diagonal size 5 m.

R005   is the ratio of the wind speed calculated by the Standard method for a panel of diagonal size 5m to the wind speed calculated by the Directional method for the same size of panel.

S010   is similar to S005 but for a panel of diagonal size 10 m.

and so on through the increasing diagonal sizes of panel.

In the rubric

H   is the Effective Height in m

VB   is the Basic (Map) Wind Speed in m/s

ALT   is the Altitude of the Site in m above sea level.

All wind speeds have been calculated for FLAT ground.

DS	100.00	100.00	100.00	100.00	100.00	100.00	100.00	100.00	100.00	100.00	100.00	100.00
DT	1.00	1.80	2.20	3.00	4.00	5.00	6.00	7.00	8.00	10.00	15.00	20.00
S005	29.00	29.00	27.20	27.20	27.20	27.20	27.20	27.20	27.20	27.20	27.20	27.20
D005	27.62	27.01	26.83	26.56	26.32	26.15	26.02	25.91	25.82	25.68	25.44	25.27
R005	1.05	1.07	1.01	1.02	1.03	1.04	1.05	1.05	1.05	1.06	1.07	1.08
S010	28.25	28.25	26.33	26.33	26.33	26.33	26.33	26.33	26.33	26.33	26.33	26.33
D010	26.37	25.79	25.61	25.36	25.13	24.97	24.84	24.74	24.65	24.52	24.29	24.13
R010	1.07	1.10	1.03	1.04	1.05	1.05	1.06	1.06	1.07	1.07	1.08	1.09
S025	27.22	27.22	25.12	25.12	25.12	25.12	25.12	25.12	25.12	25.12	25.12	25.12
D025	24.66	24.12	23.95	23.71	23.50	23.35	23.23	23.13	23.05	22.92	22.71	22.56
R025	1.10	1.13	1.05	1.06	1.07	1.08	1.08	1.09	1.09	1.10	1.11	1.11
S050	26.42	26.42	24.18	24.18	24.18	24.18	24.18	24.18	24.18	24.18	24.18	24.18
D050	23.56	23.04	22.88	22.65	22.45	22.31	22.20	22.10	22.03	21.90	21.70	21.56
R050	1.12	1.15	1.06	1.07	1.08	1.08	1.09	1.09	1.10	1.10	1.11	1.12
S100	25.59	25.59	23.19	23.19	23.19	23.19	23.19	23.19	23.19	23.19	23.19	23.19
D100	22.42	21.92	21.77	21.55	21.36	21.23	21.12	21.03	20.96	20.84	20.64	20.51
R100	1.14	1.17	1.06	1.08	1.09	1.09	1.10	1.10	1.11	1.11	1.12	1.13
S200	24.74	24.74	22.16	22.16	22.16	22.16	22.16	22.16	22.16	22.16	22.16	22.16
D200	21.21	20.74	20.60	20.39	21.21	20.08	19.98	19.90	19.83	19.72	19.53	19.41
R200	1.17	1.19	1.08	1.09	1.10	1.10	1.11	1.11	1.12	1.12	1.13	1.14

Showing effect of diagonal 'a' size
omnidirectional
H = 5.0   VB = 20.0   ALT = 0.0

DS	50.00	50.00	50.00	50.00	50.00	50.00	50.00	50.00	50.00	50.00	50.00	50.00
DT	1.00	1.80	2.20	3.00	4.00	5.00	6.00	7.00	8.00	10.00	15.00	20.00
S005	29.79	29.79	27.77	27.77	27.77	27.77	27.77	27.77	27.77	27.77	27.77	27.77
D005	28.55	27.92	27.73	27.45	27.21	27.03	26.89	26.78	26.69	26.54	26.29	26.12
R005	1.04	1.07	1.00	1.01	1.02	1.03	1.03	1.04	1.04	1.05	1.06	1.06
S010	29.02	29.02	26.88	26.88	26.88	26.88	26.88	26.88	26.88	26.88	26.88	26.88
D010	27.26	26.66	26.47	26.21	25.98	25.81	25.68	25.57	25.48	25.34	25.10	24.94
R010	1.06	1.09	1.02	1.03	1.03	1.04	1.05	1.05	1.05	1.06	1.07	1.08
S025	27.97	27.97	25.65	25.65	25.65	25.65	25.65	25.65	25.65	25.65	25.65	25.65
D025	25.48	24.92	24.75	24.50	24.29	24.13	24.01	23.91	23.83	23.69	23.47	23.32
R025	1.10	1.12	1.04	1.05	1.06	1.06	1.07	1.07	1.08	1.08	1.09	1.10
S050	27.14	27.14	24.68	24.68	24.68	24.68	24.68	24.68	24.68	24.68	24.68	24.68
D050	24.35	23.82	23.65	23.41	23.21	23.06	22.94	22.84	22.76	22.64	22.42	22.28
R050	1.11	1.14	1.04	1.05	1.06	1.07	1.08	1.08	1.08	1.09	1.10	1.11
S100	26.29	26.29	23.68	23.68	23.68	23.68	23.68	23.68	23.68	23.68	23.68	23.68
D100	23.17	22.66	22.50	22.28	22.08	21.94	21.83	21.74	21.66	21.54	21.34	21.20
R100	1.13	1.16	1.05	1.06	1.07	1.08	1.08	1.09	1.09	1.10	1.11	1.12
S200	25.41	25.41	22.62	22.62	22.62	22.62	22.62	22.62	22.62	22.62	22.62	22.62
D200	21.92	21.44	21.29	21.08	20.89	20.76	20.65	20.57	20.49	20.38	20.19	20.06
R200	1.16	1.19	1.06	1.07	1.08	1.09	1.10	1.10	1.10	1.11	1.12	1.13

Showing effect of diagonal 'a' size
omnidirectional
H = 5.0   VB = 20.0   ALT = 0.0

DS	20.00	20.00	20.00	20.00	20.00	20.00	20.00	20.00	20.00	20.00	20.00	20.00
DT	1.00	1.80	2.20	3.00	4.00	5.00	6.00	7.00	8.00	10.00	15.00	20.00
S005	30.77	30.77	28.50	28.50	28.50	28.50	28.50	28.50	28.50	28.50	28.50	28.50
D005	29.30	28.66	28.46	28.18	27.93	27.75	27.61	27.49	27.40	27.24	26.99	26.82
R005	1.05	1.07	1.00	1.01	1.02	1.03	1.03	1.04	1.04	1.05	1.06	1.06
S010	29.97	29.97	27.58	27.58	27.58	27.58	27.58	27.58	27.58	27.58	27.58	27.58
D010	27.98	27.36	27.18	26.90	26.67	26.49	26.36	26.25	26.16	26.01	25.77	25.60
R010	1.07	1.10	1.01	1.03	1.03	1.04	1.05	1.05	1.05	1.06	1.07	1.08
S025	28.88	28.88	26.32	26.32	26.32	26.32	26.32	26.32	26.32	26.32	26.32	26.32
D025	26.16	25.59	25.41	25.16	24.93	24.77	24.65	24.54	24.46	24.32	24.09	23.94
R025	1.10	1.13	1.04	1.05	1.06	1.06	1.07	1.07	1.08	1.08	1.09	1.10
S050	28.03	28.03	25.33	25.33	25.33	25.33	25.33	25.33	25.33	25.33	25.33	25.33
D050	25.00	24.45	24.28	24.03	23.82	23.67	23.55	23.45	23.37	23.24	23.02	22.87
R050	1.12	1.15	1.04	1.05	1.06	1.07	1.08	1.08	1.08	1.09	1.10	1.11
S100	27.15	27.15	24.29	24.29	24.29	24.29	24.29	24.29	24.29	24.29	24.29	24.29
D100	23.78	23.26	23.10	22.87	22.67	22.52	22.41	22.31	22.24	22.11	21.90	21.76
R100	1.14	1.17	1.05	1.06	1.07	1.08	1.08	1.09	1.09	1.10	1.11	1.12
S200	26.25	26.25	23.21	23.21	23.21	23.21	23.21	23.21	23.21	23.21	23.21	23.21
D200	22.50	22.01	21.86	21.64	21.45	21.31	21.20	21.11	21.04	20.92	20.72	20.59
R200	1.17	1.19	1.06	1.07	1.08	1.09	1.10	1.10	1.10	1.11	1.12	1.13

Showing effect of diagonal 'a' size

omnidirectional

H = 5.0   VB = 20.0   ALT = 0.0

DS	10.00	10.00	10.00	10.00	10.00	10.00	10.00	10.00	10.00	10.00	10.00	10.00
DT	0.50	1.00	1.80	2.20	3.00	4.00	5.00	6.00	7.00	8.00	10.00	1.50
S005	31.40	31.40	31.40	29.00	29.00	29.00	29.00	29.00	29.00	29.00	29.00	31.40
D005	30.41	29.56	28.91	28.71	28.42	28.17	27.99	27.85	27.73	27.64	27.48	29.10
R005	1.03	1.06	1.09	1.01	1.02	1.03	1.04	1.04	1.05	1.05	1.06	1.08
S010	30.59	30.59	30.59	28.07	28.07	28.07	28.07	28.07	28.07	28.07	28.07	30.59
D010	29.04	28.22	27.60	27.41	27.14	26.90	26.73	26.59	26.48	26.39	26.24	27.79
R010	1.05	1.08	1.11	1.02	1.03	1.04	1.05	1.06	1.06	1.06	1.07	1.10
S025	29.48	29.48	29.48	26.79	26.79	26.79	26.79	26.79	26.79	26.79	26.79	29.48
D025	27.15	26.39	25.81	25.63	25.38	25.15	24.99	24.86	24.76	24.67	24.54	25.98
R025	1.09	1.12	1.14	1.04	1.06	1.06	1.07	1.08	1.08	1.09	1.09	1.13
S050	28.61	28.61	28.61	25.78	25.78	25.78	25.78	25.78	25.78	25.78	25.78	28.61
D050	25.94	25.22	24.66	24.49	24.25	24.03	23.88	23.76	23.66	23.57	23.44	24.82
R050	1.10	1.13	1.16	1.05	1.06	1.07	1.08	1.09	1.09	1.09	1.10	1.15
S100	27.71	27.71	27.71	24.72	24.72	24.72	24.72	24.72	24.72	24.72	24.72	27.71
D100	24.68	23.99	23.47	23.30	23.07	22.87	22.72	22.60	22.51	22.43	22.31	23.62
R100	1.12	1.15	1.18	1.06	1.07	1.08	1.09	1.09	1.10	1.10	1.11	1.17
S200	26.78	26.78	26.78	23.62	23.62	23.62	23.62	23.62	23.62	23.62	23.62	26.78
D200	23.35	22.70	22.20	22.05	21.83	21.63	21.49	21.39	21.30	21.22	21.10	22.35
R200	1.15	1.18	1.21	1.07	1.08	1.09	1.10	1.10	1.11	1.11	1.12	1.20

Showing effect of diagonal 'a' size

omnidirectional

H = 5.0   VB = 20.0   ALT = 0.0

DS	5.00	5.00	5.00	5.00	5.00	5.00	5.00	5.00	5.00	5.00	5.00	5.00
DT	0.50	1.00	1.50	1.80	2.00	2.20	2.50	3.00	3.50	4.00	4.50	5.00
S005	31.91	31.91	31.91	31.91	29.45	29.45	29.45	29.45	29.45	29.45	29.45	29.45
D005	30.76	29.90	29.43	29.24	29.14	29.04	28.92	28.75	28.61	28.50	28.40	28.31
R005	1.04	1.07	1.08	1.09	1.01	1.01	1.02	1.02	1.03	1.03	1.04	1.04
S010	31.08	31.08	31.08	31.08	28.51	28.51	28.51	28.51	28.51	28.51	28.51	28.51
D010	29.37	28.55	28.11	27.92	27.82	27.73	27.61	27.45	27.32	27.21	27.12	27.03
R010	1.06	1.09	1.11	1.11	1.02	1.03	1.03	1.04	1.04	1.05	1.05	1.05
S025	29.95	29.95	29.95	29.95	27.20	27.20	27.20	27.20	27.20	27.20	27.20	27.20
D025	27.46	26.70	26.28	26.11	26.01	25.93	25.82	25.67	25.55	25.44	25.36	25.28
R025	1.09	1.12	1.14	1.15	1.05	1.05	1.05	1.06	1.06	1.07	1.07	1.08
S050	29.07	29.07	29.07	29.07	26.18	26.18	26.18	26.18	26.18	26.18	26.18	26.18
D050	26.24	25.51	25.11	24.95	24.86	24.78	24.67	24.53	24.41	24.31	24.23	24.15
R050	1.11	1.14	1.16	1.17	1.05	1.06	1.06	1.07	1.07	1.08	1.08	1.08
S100	28.16	28.16	28.16	28.16	25.11	25.11	25.11	25.11	25.11	25.11	25.11	25.11
D100	24.97	24.27	23.90	23.74	23.65	23.58	23.48	23.34	23.23	23.13	23.05	22.98
R100	1.13	1.16	1.18	1.19	1.06	1.07	1.07	1.08	1.08	1.09	1.09	1.09
S200	27.22	27.22	27.22	27.22	23.99	23.99	23.99	23.99	23.99	23.99	23.99	23.99
D200	23.63	22.97	22.61	22.46	22.38	22.31	22.21	22.08	21.98	21.89	21.81	21.75
R200	1.15	1.19	1.20	1.21	1.07	1.08	1.08	1.09	1.09	1.10	1.10	1.10

Showing effect of diagonal 'a' size
omnidirectional
H = 5.0   VB = 20.0   ALT = 0.0

DS	2.00	2.00	2.00	2.00	2.00	2.00	2.00	2.00	2.00	2.00	2.00	2.00
DT	0.00	0.10	0.20	0.40	0.60	0.80	1.00	1.20	1.40	1.60	1.80	2.00
S005	32.40	32.40	32.40	32.40	32.40	32.40	32.40	32.40	32.40	32.40	32.40	30.00
D005	32.41	31.90	32.06	31.70	31.23	30.86	30.58	30.35	30.18	30.03	29.90	29.79
R005	1.00	1.02	1.01	1.02	1.04	1.05	1.06	1.07	1.07	1.08	1.08	1.01
S010	31.56	31.56	31.56	31.56	31.56	31.56	31.56	31.56	31.56	31.56	31.56	29.04
D010	31.29	30.56	30.65	30.27	29.82	29.46	29.19	28.98	28.81	28.67	28.55	28.45
R010	1.01	1.03	1.03	1.04	1.06	1.07	1.08	1.09	1.10	1.10	1.11	1.02
S025	30.41	30.41	30.41	30.41	30.41	30.41	30.41	30.41	30.41	30.41	30.41	27.71
D025	29.74	28.71	28.71	28.30	27.88	27.55	27.29	27.10	26.94	26.80	26.69	26.59
R025	1.02	1.06	1.06	1.07	1.09	1.10	1.11	1.12	1.13	1.13	1.14	1.04
S050	29.52	29.52	29.52	29.52	29.52	29.52	29.52	29.52	29.52	29.52	29.52	26.66
D050	28.75	27.53	27.46	27.04	26.63	26.32	26.07	25.89	25.74	25.61	25.50	25.41
R050	1.03	1.07	1.07	1.09	1.11	1.12	1.13	1.14	1.15	1.15	1.16	1.05
S100	28.59	28.59	28.59	28.59	28.59	28.59	28.59	28.59	28.59	28.59	28.59	25.58
D100	27.72	26.30	26.17	25.73	25.34	25.04	24.81	24.63	24.48	24.37	24.26	24.17
R100	1.03	1.09	1.09	1.11	1.13	1.14	1.15	1.16	1.17	1.17	1.18	1.06
S200	27.64	27.64	27.64	27.64	27.64	27.64	27.64	27.64	27.64	27.64	27.64	24.44
D200	26.63	25.00	24.80	24.35	23.97	23.68	23.47	23.30	23.16	23.05	22.95	22.87
R200	1.04	1.11	1.11	1.14	1.15	1.17	1.18	1.19	1.19	1.20	1.20	1.07

Showing effect of diagonal 'a' size
omnidirectional
H = 5.0   VB = 20.0   ALT = 0.0

DS	100.00	100.00	100.00	100.00	100.00	100.00	100.00	100.00	100.00	100.00	100.00	100.00
DT	1.00	1.80	2.20	3.00	4.00	5.00	6.00	7.00	8.00	10.00	15.00	20.00
S005	35.40	35.40	35.40	35.40	35.40	35.40	35.40	35.40	35.40	35.40	35.40	35.40
D005	35.46	35.57	35.30	35.13	34.91	34.71	34.53	34.38	34.25	34.04	33.71	33.50
R005	1.00	1.00	1.00	1.01	1.01	1.02	1.03	1.03	1.04	1.04	1.05	1.06
S010	34.48	34.48	34.48	34.48	34.48	34.48	34.48	34.48	34.48	34.48	34.48	34.48
D010	34.56	34.46	34.38	34.21	33.99	33.79	33.62	33.47	33.35	33.15	32.82	32.61
R010	1.00	1.00	1.00	1.01	1.01	1.02	1.03	1.03	1.03	1.04	1.05	1.06
S025	33.23	33.23	33.23	33.23	33.23	33.23	33.23	33.23	33.23	33.23	33.23	33.23
D025	33.00	32.86	32.77	32.60	32.39	32.20	32.03	31.89	31.77	31.58	31.27	31.08
R025	1.01	1.01	1.01	1.02	1.03	1.03	1.04	1.04	1.05	1.05	1.06	1.07
S050	32.25	32.25	32.25	32.25	32.25	32.25	32.25	32.25	32.25	32.25	32.25	32.25
D050	31.61	31.44	31.36	31.18	30.97	30.79	30.63	30.50	30.38	30.20	29.90	29.72
R050	1.02	1.03	1.03	1.03	1.04	1.05	1.05	1.06	1.06	1.07	1.08	1.09
S100	31.24	31.24	31.24	31.24	31.24	31.24	31.24	31.24	31.24	31.24	31.24	31.24
D100	30.21	30.01	29.92	29.74	29.53	29.36	29.21	29.08	28.97	28.80	28.52	28.34
R100	1.03	1.04	1.04	1.05	1.06	1.06	1.07	1.07	1.08	1.08	1.10	1.10
S200	30.20	30.20	30.20	30.20	30.20	30.20	30.20	30.20	30.20	30.20	30.20	30.20
D200	29.18	28.95	28.86	28.68	28.48	28.31	28.16	28.04	27.93	27.77	27.50	27.32
R200	1.03	1.04	1.05	1.05	1.06	1.07	1.07	1.08	1.08	1.09	1.10	1.11

Showing effect of diagonal 'a' size
omnidirectional
H = 20.0   VB = 20.0   ALT = 0.0

DS	50.00	50.00	50.00	50.00	50.00	50.00	50.00	50.00	50.00	50.00	50.00	50.00
DT	1.00	1.80	2.20	3.00	4.00	5.00	6.00	7.00	8.00	10.00	15.00	20.00
S005	36.29	36.29	36.29	36.29	36.29	36.29	36.29	36.29	36.29	36.29	36.29	36.29
D005	36.54	36.45	36.37	36.19	35.96	35.76	35.57	35.42	35.29	35.07	34.73	34.51
R005	0.99	1.00	1.00	1.00	1.01	1.02	1.02	1.02	1.03	1.03	1.05	1.05
S010	35.35	35.35	35.35	35.35	35.35	35.35	35.35	35.35	35.35	35.35	35.35	35.35
D010	35.62	35.51	35.42	35.25	35.02	34.82	34.64	34.49	34.36	34.15	33.82	33.06
R010	0.99	1.00	1.00	1.00	1.01	1.02	1.02	1.03	1.03	1.04	1.05	1.05
S025	34.07	34.07	34.07	34.07	34.07	34.07	34.07	34.07	34.07	34.07	34.07	34.07
D025	34.01	33.86	33.78	33.60	33.38	33.18	33.01	32.87	32.75	32.55	32.23	32.03
R025	1.00	1.01	1.01	1.01	1.02	1.03	1.03	1.04	1.04	1.05	1.06	1.06
S050	33.07	33.07	33.07	33.07	33.07	33.07	33.07	33.07	33.07	33.07	33.07	33.07
D050	32.59	32.41	32.32	32.14	31.93	31.74	31.57	31.44	31.32	31.13	30.82	30.63
R050	1.01	1.02	1.02	1.03	1.04	1.04	1.05	1.05	1.06	1.06	1.07	1.08
S100	32.03	32.03	32.03	32.03	32.03	32.03	32.03	32.03	32.03	32.03	32.03	32.03
D100	31.15	30.94	30.85	30.66	30.45	30.27	30.11	29.98	29.87	29.69	29.40	29.22
R100	1.03	1.04	1.04	1.04	1.05	1.06	1.06	1.07	1.07	1.08	1.09	1.10
S200	30.96	30.96	30.96	30.96	30.96	30.96	30.96	30.96	30.96	30.96	30.96	30.96
D200	30.09	29.86	29.76	29.57	29.37	29.19	29.04	28.92	28.81	28.63	28.35	28.18
R200	1.03	1.04	1.04	1.05	1.05	1.06	1.07	1.07	1.07	1.08	1.09	1.10

Showing effect of diagonal 'a' size
omnidirectional
H = 20.0   VB = 20.0   ALT = 0.0

DS	20.00	20.00	20.00	20.00	20.00	20.00	20.00	20.00	20.00	20.00	20.00	20.00
DT	1.00	1.80	2.20	3.00	4.00	5.00	6.00	7.00	8.00	10.00	15.00	20.00
S005	37.30	37.30	37.30	37.30	37.30	37.30	37.30	37.30	37.30	37.30	37.30	37.30
D005	37.45	37.35	37.27	37.09	36.86	36.64	36.46	36.30	36.16	35.94	35.59	35.37
R005	1.00	1.00	1.00	1.01	1.01	1.02	1.02	1.03	1.03	1.04	1.05	1.05
S010	36.33	36.33	36.33	36.33	36.33	36.33	36.33	36.33	36.33	36.33	36.33	36.33
D010	36.51	36.39	36.31	36.13	35.89	35.69	35.51	35.35	35.22	35.00	34.66	34.44
R010	1.00	1.00	1.00	1.01	1.01	1.02	1.02	1.03	1.03	1.04	1.05	1.05
S025	35.02	35.02	35.02	35.02	35.02	35.02	35.02	35.02	35.02	35.02	35.02	35.02
D025	34.87	34.72	34.63	34.44	34.22	34.01	33.84	33.69	33.57	33.36	33.04	32.83
R025	1.00	1.01	1.01	1.02	1.02	1.03	1.03	1.04	1.04	1.05	1.06	1.07
S050	33.98	33.98	33.98	33.98	33.98	33.98	33.98	33.98	33.98	33.98	33.98	33.98
D050	33.42	33.23	33.14	32.95	32.73	32.54	32.37	32.23	32.11	31.92	31.60	31.40
R050	1.02	1.02	1.03	1.03	1.04	1.04	1.05	1.05	1.06	1.06	1.08	1.08
S100	32.92	32.92	32.92	32.92	32.92	32.92	32.92	32.92	32.92	32.92	32.92	32.92
D100	31.95	31.73	31.63	31.44	31.23	31.04	30.88	30.75	30.63	30.45	30.15	29.96
R100	1.03	1.04	1.04	1.05	1.05	1.06	1.07	1.07	1.07	1.08	1.09	1.10
S200	31.82	31.82	31.82	31.82	31.82	31.82	31.82	31.82	31.82	31.82	31.82	31.82
D200	30.87	30.63	30.52	30.33	30.12	29.94	29.78	29.65	29.54	29.37	29.08	28.90
R200	1.03	1.04	1.04	1.05	1.06	1.06	1.07	1.07	1.08	1.08	1.09	1.10

Showing effect of diagonal 'a' size
omnidirectional
H = 20.0   VB = 20.0   ALT = 0.0

DS	10.00	10.00	10.00	10.00	10.00	10.00	10.00	10.00	10.00	10.00	10.00	10.00
DT	0.50	1.00	1.50	1.80	2.20	3.00	4.00	5.00	6.00	7.00	8.00	10.00
S005	37.80	37.80	37.80	37.80	37.80	37.80	37.80	37.80	37.80	37.80	37.80	37.80
D005	37.60	37.67	37.62	37.57	37.49	37.31	37.07	36.86	36.67	36.51	36.37	36.15
R005	1.01	1.00	1.00	1.01	1.01	1.01	1.02	1.03	1.03	1.04	1.04	1.05
S010	36.82	36.82	36.82	36.82	36.82	36.82	36.82	36.82	36.82	36.82	36.82	36.82
D010	36.69	36.73	36.66	36.61	36.53	36.34	36.11	35.90	35.72	35.56	35.43	35.21
R010	1.00	1.00	1.00	1.01	1.01	1.01	1.02	1.03	1.03	1.04	1.04	1.05
S025	35.48	35.48	35.48	35.48	35.48	35.48	35.48	35.48	35.48	35.48	35.48	35.48
D025	35.12	35.08	34.99	34.93	34.84	34.65	34.42	34.22	34.05	33.90	33.77	33.57
R025	1.01	1.01	1.01	1.02	1.02	1.02	1.03	1.04	1.04	1.05	1.05	1.06
S050	34.44	34.44	34.44	34.44	34.44	34.44	34.44	34.44	34.44	34.44	34.44	34.44
D050	33.73	33.63	33.51	33.44	33.35	33.16	32.93	32.74	32.57	32.43	32.31	32.11
R050	1.02	1.02	1.03	1.03	1.03	1.04	1.05	1.05	1.06	1.06	1.07	1.07
S100	33.36	33.36	33.36	33.36	33.36	33.36	33.36	33.36	33.36	33.36	33.36	33.36
D100	32.32	32.15	32.01	31.93	31.83	31.64	31.42	31.24	31.08	30.94	30.82	30.64
R100	1.03	1.04	1.04	1.04	1.05	1.05	1.06	1.07	1.07	1.08	1.08	1.09
S200	32.24	32.24	32.24	32.24	32.24	32.24	32.24	32.24	32.24	32.24	32.24	32.24
D200	31.29	31.07	30.91	30.82	30.72	30.53	30.31	30.13	29.98	29.85	29.73	29.56
R200	1.03	1.04	1.04	1.05	1.05	1.06	1.06	1.07	1.08	1.08	1.08	1.09

Showing effect of diagonal 'a' size
omnidirectional
H = 20.0   VB = 20.0   ALT = 0.0

DS	5.00	5.00	5.00	5.00	5.00	5.00	5.00	5.00	5.00	5.00	5.00	5.00
DT	0.50	1.00	1.50	1.80	2.00	2.20	2.50	3.00	3.50	4.00	4.50	5.00
S005	38.00	38.00	38.00	38.00	38.00	38.00	38.00	38.00	38.00	38.00	38.00	38.00
D005	37.64	37.70	37.65	37.60	37.56	37.51	37.45	37.33	37.21	37.09	36.98	36.88
R005	1.01	1.01	1.01	1.01	1.01	1.01	1.01	1.02	1.02	1.02	1.03	1.03
S010	37.19	37.19	37.19	37.19	37.19	37.19	37.19	37.19	37.19	37.19	37.19	37.19
D010	36.74	36.76	36.70	36.64	36.60	36.55	36.49	36.37	36.25	36.13	36.03	35.92
R010	1.01	1.01	1.01	1.02	1.02	1.02	1.02	1.02	1.03	1.03	1.03	1.04
S025	36.09	36.09	36.09	36.09	36.09	36.09	36.09	36.09	36.09	36.09	36.09	36.09
D025	35.18	35.13	35.04	34.97	34.93	34.88	34.81	34.69	34.58	34.46	34.36	34.26
R025	1.03	1.03	1.03	1.03	1.03	1.03	1.04	1.04	1.04	1.05	1.05	1.05
S050	35.24	35.24	35.24	35.24	35.24	35.24	35.24	35.24	35.24	35.24	35.24	35.24
D050	33.80	33.69	33.57	33.50	33.45	33.40	33.33	33.21	33.10	32.99	32.89	32.79
R050	1.04	1.05	1.05	1.05	1.05	1.06	1.06	1.06	1.06	1.07	1.07	1.07
S100	34.37	34.37	34.37	34.37	34.37	34.37	34.37	34.37	34.37	34.37	34.37	34.37
D100	32.41	32.23	32.08	32.00	31.95	31.90	31.82	31.71	31.59	31.49	31.39	31.30
R100	1.06	1.07	1.07	1.07	1.08	1.08	1.08	1.08	1.09	1.09	1.09	1.10
S200	33.47	33.47	33.47	33.47	33.47	33.47	33.47	33.47	33.47	33.47	33.47	33.47
D200	31.38	31.15	30.99	30.90	30.85	30.79	30.72	30.60	30.49	30.39	30.29	30.20
R200	1.07	1.07	1.08	1.08	1.08	1.09	1.09	1.09	1.10	1.10	1.10	1.11

Showing effect of diagonal 'a' size
omnidirectional
H = 20.0   VB = 20.0   ALT = 0.0

DS	2.00	2.00	2.00	2.00	2.00	2.00	2.00	2.00	2.00	2.00	2.00	2.00
DT	0.00	0.10	0.20	0.40	0.60	0.80	1.00	1.20	1.40	1.60	1.80	2.00
S005	38.00	38.00	38.00	38.00	38.00	38.00	38.00	38.00	38.00	38.00	38.00	38.00
D005	37.95	37.34	37.49	37.62	37.67	37.69	37.68	37.66	37.64	37.60	37.56	37.52
R005	1.00	1.02	1.01	1.01	1.01	1.01	1.01	1.01	1.01	1.01	1.01	1.01
S010	37.19	37.19	37.19	37.19	37.19	37.19	37.19	37.19	37.19	37.19	37.19	37.19
D010	37.19	36.59	36.69	36.76	36.79	36.79	36.77	36.75	36.71	36.67	36.63	36.59
R010	1.00	1.02	1.01	1.01	1.01	1.01	1.01	1.01	1.01	1.01	1.02	1.02
S025	36.09	36.09	36.09	36.09	36.09	36.09	36.09	36.09	36.09	36.09	36.09	36.09
D025	35.86	35.29	35.29	35.27	35.25	35.22	35.19	35.14	35.10	35.05	35.01	34.96
R025	1.01	1.02	1.02	1.02	1.02	1.02	1.03	1.03	1.03	1.03	1.03	1.03
S050	35.24	35.24	35.24	35.24	35.24	35.24	35.24	35.24	35.24	35.24	35.24	35.24
D050	34.69	34.13	34.05	33.96	33.89	33.84	33.78	33.73	33.68	33.62	33.57	33.52
R050	1.02	1.03	1.03	1.04	1.04	1.04	1.04	1.04	1.05	1.05	1.05	1.05
S100	34.37	34.37	34.37	34.37	34.37	34.37	34.37	34.37	34.37	34.37	34.37	34.37
D100	33.50	32.96	32.80	32.62	32.52	32.43	32.36	32.29	32.23	32.17	32.12	32.06
R100	1.03	1.04	1.05	1.05	1.06	1.06	1.06	1.06	1.07	1.07	1.07	1.07
S200	33.47	33.47	33.47	33.47	33.47	33.47	33.47	33.47	33.47	33.47	33.47	33.47
D200	32.62	32.10	31.87	31.64	31.50	31.40	31.31	31.24	31.17	31.11	31.05	30.99
R200	1.03	1.04	1.05	1.06	1.06	1.07	1.07	1.07	1.07	1.08	1.08	1.08

Showing effect of diagonal 'a' size
omnidirectional
H = 20.0   VB = 20.0   ALT = 0.0

DS	100.00	100.00	100.00	100.00	100.00	100.00	100.00	100.00	100.00	100.00	100.00	100.00
DT	1.00	1.80	2.20	3.00	4.00	5.00	6.00	7.00	8.00	10.00	15.00	20.00
S005	41.40	41.40	41.40	41.40	41.40	41.40	41.40	41.40	41.40	41.40	41.40	41.40
D005	40.92	41.03	41.07	41.15	41.23	41.29	41.34	41.38	41.42	41.47	41.54	41.56
R005	1.01	1.01	1.01	1.01	1.00	1.00	1.00	1.00	1.00	1.00	1.00	1.00
S010	40.33	40.33	40.33	40.33	40.33	40.33	40.33	40.33	40.33	40.33	40.33	40.33
D010	40.51	40.60	40.64	40.70	40.77	40.82	40.87	40.91	40.94	40.98	41.04	41.06
R010	1.00	0.99	0.99	0.99	0.99	0.99	0.99	0.99	0.99	0.98	0.98	0.98
S025	38.86	38.86	38.86	38.86	38.86	38.86	38.86	38.86	38.86	38.86	38.86	38.86
D025	39.21	39.24	39.25	39.27	39.30	39.34	39.36	39.39	39.40	39.43	39.45	39.46
R025	0.99	0.99	0.99	0.99	0.99	0.99	0.99	0.99	0.99	0.99	0.98	0.98
S050	37.72	37.72	37.72	37.72	37.72	37.72	37.72	37.72	37.72	37.72	37.72	37.72
D050	38.15	38.13	38.11	38.10	38.11	38.12	38.13	38.14	38.15	38.16	38.16	38.15
R050	0.99	0.99	0.99	0.99	0.99	0.99	0.99	0.99	0.99	0.99	0.99	0.99
S100	36.54	36.54	36.54	36.54	36.54	36.54	36.54	36.54	36.54	36.54	36.54	36.54
D100	37.06	36.98	36.95	36.90	36.88	36.87	36.87	36.87	36.87	36.86	36.83	36.80
R100	0.99	0.99	0.99	0.99	0.99	0.99	0.99	0.99	0.99	0.99	0.99	0.99
S200	35.32	35.32	35.32	35.32	35.32	35.32	35.32	35.32	35.32	35.32	35.32	35.32
D200	36.09	35.97	35.92	35.84	35.79	35.77	35.75	35.74	35.73	35.71	35.66	35.61
R200	0.98	0.98	0.98	0.99	0.99	0.99	0.99	0.99	0.99	0.99	0.99	0.99

Showing effect of diagonal 'a' size
omnidirectional
H = 100.0　VB = 20.0　ALT = 0.0

DS	50.00	50.00	50.00	50.00	50.00	50.00	50.00	50.00	50.00	50.00	50.00	50.00
DT	1.00	1.80	2.20	3.00	4.00	5.00	6.00	7.00	8.00	10.00	15.00	20.00
S005	41.78	41.78	41.78	41.78	41.78	41.78	41.78	41.78	41.78	41.78	41.78	41.78
D005	41.67	41.75	41.78	41.84	41.90	41.95	42.00	42.03	42.06	42.10	42.16	42.17
R005	1.00	1.00	1.00	1.00	1.00	1.00	0.99	0.99	0.99	0.99	0.99	0.99
S010	40.89	40.89	40.89	40.89	40.89	40.89	40.89	40.89	40.89	40.89	40.89	40.89
D010	41.27	41.33	41.35	41.40	41.45	41.50	41.53	41.56	41.59	41.63	41.67	41.68
R010	0.99	0.99	0.99	0.99	0.99	0.99	0.98	0.98	0.98	0.98	0.98	0.98
S025	39.69	39.69	39.69	39.69	39.69	39.69	39.69	39.69	39.69	39.69	39.69	39.69
D025	40.00	40.00	39.99	40.00	40.02	40.04	40.06	40.07	40.09	40.11	40.12	40.11
R025	0.99	0.99	0.99	0.99	0.99	0.99	0.99	0.99	0.99	0.99	0.99	0.99
S050	38.75	38.75	38.75	38.75	38.75	38.75	38.75	38.75	38.75	38.75	38.75	38.75
D050	38.96	38.91	38.88	38.85	38.85	38.85	38.85	38.86	38.86	38.86	38.85	38.83
R050	0.99	1.00	1.00	1.00	1.00	1.00	1.00	1.00	1.00	1.00	1.00	1.00
S100	37.79	37.79	37.79	37.79	37.79	37.79	37.79	37.79	37.79	37.79	37.79	37.79
D100	37.89	37.79	37.74	37.68	37.64	37.62	37.61	37.61	37.60	37.59	37.55	37.51
R100	1.00	1.00	1.00	1.00	1.00	1.00	1.00	1.00	1.00	1.01	1.01	1.01
S200	36.80	36.80	36.80	36.80	36.80	36.80	36.80	36.80	36.80	36.80	36.80	36.80
D200	36.94	36.79	36.73	36.64	36.58	36.54	36.52	36.50	36.48	36.46	36.39	36.34
R200	1.00	1.00	1.00	1.00	1.01	1.01	1.01	1.01	1.01	1.01	1.01	1.01

Showing effect of diagonal 'a' size
omnidirectional
H = 100.0　VB = 20.0　ALT = 0.0

DS	20.00	20.00	20.00	20.00	20.00	20.00	20.00	20.00	20.00	20.00	20.00	20.00
DT	1.00	1.80	2.20	3.00	4.00	5.00	6.00	7.00	8.00	10.00	15.00	20.00
S005	42.21	42.21	42.21	42.21	42.21	42.21	42.21	42.21	42.21	42.21	42.21	42.21
D005	42.01	42.04	42.06	42.09	42.13	42.17	42.20	42.23	42.25	42.28	42.31	42.32
R005	1.00	1.00	1.00	1.00	1.00	1.00	1.00	1.00	1.00	1.00	1.00	1.00
S010	41.31	41.31	41.31	41.31	41.31	41.31	41.31	41.31	41.31	41.31	41.31	41.31
D010	41.62	41.64	41.65	41.67	41.70	41.73	41.76	41.78	41.80	41.82	41.84	41.84
R010	0.99	0.99	0.99	0.99	0.99	0.99	0.99	0.99	0.99	0.99	0.99	0.99
S025	40.09	40.09	40.09	40.09	40.09	40.09	40.09	40.09	40.09	40.09	40.09	40.09
D025	40.40	40.36	40.35	40.33	40.32	40.33	40.34	40.35	40.36	40.36	40.36	40.34
R025	0.99	0.99	0.99	0.99	0.99	0.99	0.99	0.99	0.99	0.99	0.99	0.99
S050	39.14	39.14	39.14	39.14	39.14	39.14	39.14	39.14	39.14	39.14	39.14	39.14
D050	39.40	39.32	39.28	39.23	39.20	39.19	39.19	39.18	39.18	39.17	39.14	39.11
R050	0.99	1.00	1.00	1.00	1.00	1.00	1.00	1.00	1.00	1.00	1.00	1.00
S100	38.17	38.17	38.17	38.17	38.17	38.17	38.17	38.17	38.17	38.17	38.17	38.17
D100	38.38	38.25	38.19	38.10	38.05	38.02	38.00	37.99	37.97	37.95	37.89	37.84
R100	0.99	1.00	1.00	1.00	1.00	1.00	1.00	1.00	1.01	1.01	1.01	1.01
S200	37.17	37.17	37.17	37.17	37.17	37.17	37.17	37.17	37.17	37.17	37.17	37.17
D200	37.47	37.30	37.22	37.11	37.03	36.98	36.95	36.92	36.90	36.87	36.79	36.72
R200	0.99	1.00	1.00	1.00	1.00	1.01	1.01	1.01	1.01	1.01	1.01	1.01

Showing effect of diagonal 'a' size
omnidirectional
H = 100.0   VB = 20.0   ALT = 0.0

DS	10.00	10.00	10.00	10.00	10.00	10.00	10.00	10.00	10.00	10.00	10.00	10.00
DT	0.50	1.00	1.80	2.20	3.00	4.00	5.00	6.00	7.00	8.00	10.00	1.50
S005	42.40	42.40	42.40	42.40	42.40	42.40	42.40	42.40	42.40	42.40	42.40	42.40
D005	41.77	41.78	41.78	41.78	41.79	41.82	41.84	41.87	41.89	41.90	41.92	41.78
R005	1.02	1.01	1.01	1.01	1.01	1.01	1.01	1.01	1.01	1.01	1.01	1.01
S010	41.50	41.50	41.50	41.50	41.50	41.50	41.50	41.50	41.50	41.50	41.50	41.50
D010	41.41	41.41	41.40	41.39	41.39	41.40	41.42	41.44	41.46	41.47	41.49	41.40
R010	1.00	1.00	1.00	1.00	1.00	1.00	1.00	1.00	1.00	1.00	1.00	1.00
S025	40.27	40.27	40.27	40.27	40.27	40.27	40.27	40.27	40.27	40.27	40.27	40.27
D025	40.25	40.24	40.18	40.15	40.11	40.09	40.09	40.09	40.09	40.10	40.09	40.20
R025	1.00	1.00	1.00	1.00	1.00	1.00	1.00	1.00	1.00	1.00	1.00	1.00
S050	39.32	39.32	39.32	39.32	39.32	39.32	39.32	39.32	39.32	39.32	39.32	39.32
D050	39.31	39.29	39.18	39.13	39.06	39.02	39.00	38.99	38.98	38.97	38.96	39.22
R050	1.00	1.00	1.00	1.00	1.01	1.01	1.01	1.01	1.01	1.01	1.01	1.00
S100	38.34	38.34	38.34	38.34	38.34	38.34	38.34	38.34	38.34	38.34	38.34	38.34
D100	38.34	38.31	38.15	38.08	37.99	37.92	37.88	37.85	37.83	37.82	37.79	38.21
R100	1.00	1.00	1.01	1.01	1.01	1.01	1.01	1.01	1.01	1.01	1.01	1.00
S200	37.34	37.34	37.34	37.34	37.34	37.34	37.34	37.34	37.34	37.34	37.34	37.34
D200	37.48	37.44	37.25	37.16	37.03	36.94	36.89	36.85	36.82	36.80	36.75	37.32
R200	1.00	1.00	1.00	1.00	1.01	1.01	1.01	1.01	1.01	1.01	1.02	1.00

Showing effect of diagonal 'a' size
omnidirectional
H = 100.0   VB = 20.0   ALT = 0.0

DS	5.00	5.00	5.00	5.00	5.00	5.00	5.00	5.00	5.00	5.00	5.00	5.00
DT	0.50	1.00	1.50	1.80	2.00	2.20	2.50	3.00	3.50	4.00	4.50	5.00
S005	42.45	42.45	42.45	42.45	42.45	42.45	42.45	42.45	42.45	42.45	42.45	42.45
D005	41.54	41.53	41.52	41.50	41.50	41.49	41.49	41.48	41.48	41.49	41.49	41.50
R005	1.02	1.02	1.02	1.02	1.02	1.02	1.02	1.02	1.02	1.02	1.02	1.02
S010	41.55	41.55	41.55	41.55	41.55	41.55	41.55	41.55	41.55	41.55	41.55	41.55
D010	41.19	41.18	41.16	41.14	41.13	41.12	41.11	41.10	41.09	41.09	41.10	41.10
R010	1.01	1.01	1.01	1.01	1.01	1.01	1.01	1.01	1.01	1.01	1.01	1.01
S025	40.32	40.32	40.32	40.32	40.32	40.32	40.32	40.32	40.32	40.32	40.32	40.32
D025	40.09	40.07	40.02	39.98	39.96	39.94	39.91	39.88	39.86	39.85	39.84	39.83
R025	1.01	1.01	1.01	1.01	1.01	1.01	1.01	1.01	1.01	1.01	1.01	1.01
S050	39.37	39.37	39.37	39.37	39.37	39.37	39.37	39.37	39.37	39.37	39.37	39.37
D050	39.19	39.17	39.08	39.03	39.00	38.97	38.94	38.89	38.85	38.83	38.81	38.80
R050	1.00	1.01	1.01	1.01	1.01	1.01	1.01	1.01	1.01	1.01	1.01	1.01
S100	38.39	38.39	38.39	38.39	38.39	38.39	38.39	38.39	38.39	38.39	38.39	38.39
D100	38.27	38.24	38.13	38.06	38.02	37.98	37.93	37.86	37.82	37.78	37.76	37.73
R100	1.00	1.00	1.01	1.01	1.01	1.01	1.01	1.01	1.02	1.02	1.02	1.02
S200	37.39	37.39	37.39	37.39	37.39	37.39	37.39	37.39	37.39	37.39	37.39	37.39
D200	37.45	37.42	37.28	37.20	37.15	37.10	37.04	36.96	36.90	36.86	36.82	36.79
R200	1.00	1.00	1.00	1.01	1.01	1.01	1.01	1.01	1.01	1.01	1.02	1.02

Showing effect of diagonal 'a' size
omnidirectional
H = 100.0   VB = 20.0   ALT = 0.0

DS	2.00	2.00	2.00	2.00	2.00	2.00	2.00	2.00	2.00	2.00	2.00	2.00
DT	0.00	0.10	0.20	0.40	0.60	0.80	1.00	1.20	1.40	1.60	1.80	2.00
S005	42.40	42.40	42.40	42.40	42.40	42.40	42.40	42.40	42.40	42.40	42.40	42.40
D005	42.37	41.69	41.69	41.70	41.70	41.70	41.69	41.68	41.67	41.66	41.64	41.63
R005	1.00	1.02	1.02	1.02	1.02	1.02	1.02	1.02	1.02	1.02	1.02	1.02
S010	41.50	41.50	41.50	41.50	41.50	41.50	41.50	41.50	41.50	41.50	41.50	41.50
D010	42.02	41.35	41.35	41.36	41.36	41.36	41.35	41.34	41.32	41.30	41.29	41.27
R010	0.99	1.00	1.00	1.00	1.00	1.00	1.00	1.00	1.00	1.00	1.01	1.01
S025	40.27	40.27	40.27	40.27	40.27	40.27	40.27	40.27	40.27	40.27	40.27	40.27
R025	40.93	40.27	40.27	40.28	40.29	40.29	40.27	40.25	40.22	40.19	40.16	40.13
R025	0.98	1.00	1.00	1.00	1.00	1.00	1.00	1.00	1.00	1.00	1.00	1.00
S050	39.32	39.32	39.32	39.32	39.32	39.32	39.32	39.32	39.32	39.32	39.32	39.32
D050	40.03	39.39	39.38	39.41	39.42	39.41	39.39	39.35	39.31	39.27	39.24	39.20
R050	0.98	1.00	1.00	1.00	1.00	1.00	1.00	1.00	1.00	1.00	1.00	1.00
S100	38.34	38.34	38.34	38.34	38.34	38.34	38.34	38.34	38.34	38.34	38.34	38.34
D100	39.11	38.48	38.47	38.50	38.52	38.52	38.48	38.44	38.39	38.34	38.29	38.24
R100	0.98	1.00	1.00	1.00	1.00	1.00	1.00	1.00	1.00	1.00	1.00	1.00
S200	37.34	37.34	37.34	37.34	37.34	37.34	37.34	37.34	37.34	37.34	37.34	37.34
D200	38.29	37.68	37.67	37.71	37.73	37.72	37.68	37.63	37.57	37.51	37.45	37.39
R200	0.98	0.99	0.99	0.99	0.99	0.99	0.99	0.99	0.99	1.00	1.00	1.00

Showing effect of diagonal 'a' size
omnidirectional
H = 100.0   VB = 20.0   ALT = 0.0

Group 1. Section 2. Wind speed calculations

In this second section (pp. 84–94) values of wind speed calculated by both methods are given for a range of wind directions.

The columns are numbered across the top from 0 to 330 (in multiples of 30). These are values of wind direction in degrees east of north.
The rows of data are as follows:

DS is the distance from the sea in km
DT is the distance within a town in km.
VE is the peak gust wind speed calculated by the Directional method for a value of the diagonal 'a' of the first value to appear in the rubric under each set of values, which is normally the panel size 5 m.
VI is the peak gust wind speed calculated by the Directional method for a value of the diagonal 'a' of the second value to appear in the rubric under each set of values, which is normally the value for the internal volume.
VO is the peak gust wind speed calculated by the Directional method for the third value of diagonal 'a' to appear in the rubric under each set of values, which is normally the value for the overall building.
V1 is the peak gust wind speed calculated by the Standard method for a value of the diagonal 'a' of the first value to appear in the rubric under each set of values.
V2 is the peak gust wind speed calculated by the Standard method for a value of the diagonal 'a' of the second value to appear in the rubric under each set of values.

In the rubric the following symbols are used:

H is the effective height in m
a gives three values of the diagonal 'a' in m.
VB gives the basic wind speed from the map of Figure 6.
ALT gives the altitude of the site in m above sea level.

At the bottom of each page a description of the site in its surroundings is given and in the right hand margin are sketches showing where the site is either with respect to the coastline, or its position in the town.

In the Standard method the allowance for diagonal size is not accounted for in the calculation of wind speed, but is allowed for by the use of the size factor (C_a) in the calculation of pressure. To allow a comparison of the values obtained by the two methods, the values of wind speed calculated by the Standard method for a diagonal a size of 5 m have been multiplied by the square root of C_a appropriate to the value of 'a' appearing in the rubric.

Wind direction

	0	30	60	90	120	150	180	210	240	270	300	330
DS	100.00	100.00	100.00	100.00	100.00	100.00	100.00	100.00	100.00	100.00	100.00	100.00
DT	0.30	0.30	0.30	0.30	0.30	0.30	0.30	0.30	0.30	0.30	0.30	0.30
VE	22.50	21.06	21.06	21.34	21.06	23.07	24.52	26.82	28.84	28.56	26.25	23.65
VI	17.32	16.21	16.21	16.43	16.21	17.77	18.88	20.65	22.21	21.99	20.21	18.21
VO	19.22	17.99	17.99	18.23	17.99	19.71	20.95	22.92	24.64	24.40	22.42	20.21
V1	22.62	21.17	21.17	21.46	21.17	23.20	24.65	26.97	29.00	28.71	26.39	23.78
V2	19.30	18.06	18.06	18.31	18.06	19.79	21.03	23.01	24.74	24.49	22.51	20.28

H = 5.0   VB = 20.0   ALT = 0.0

Wind direction

	0	30	60	90	120	150	180	210	240	270	300	330
DS	100.00	100.00	100.00	100.00	100.00	100.00	100.00	100.00	100.00	100.00	100.00	100.00
DT	1.80	1.80	1.80	1.80	1.80	1.80	1.80	1.80	1.80	1.80	1.80	1.80
VE	21.07	19.72	19.72	19.99	19.72	21.61	22.96	25.12	27.01	26.74	24.58	22.15
VI	16.18	15.14	15.14	15.35	15.14	16.60	17.63	19.29	20.74	20.54	18.88	17.01
VO	17.97	16.82	16.82	17.05	16.82	18.43	19.59	21.43	23.04	22.81	20.97	18.89
V1	22.62	21.17	21.17	21.46	21.17	23.20	24.65	26.97	29.00	28.71	26.39	23.78
V2	19.30	18.06	18.06	18.31	18.06	19.79	21.03	23.01	24.74	24.49	22.51	20.08

H = 5.0   VB = 20.0   ALT = 0.0

Wind direction

	0	30	60	90	120	150	180	210	240	270	300	330
DS	100.00	100.00	100.00	100.00	100.00	100.00	100.00	100.00	100.00	100.00	100.00	100.00
DT	2.50	2.50	2.50	2.50	2.50	2.50	2.50	2.50	2.50	2.50	2.50	2.50
VE	20.84	19.50	19.50	19.77	19.50	21.37	22.71	24.84	26.71	26.45	24.31	21.90
VI	16.00	14.98	14.98	15.18	14.98	16.41	17.44	19.08	20.51	20.31	18.67	16.82
VO	17.77	16.63	16.63	16.86	16.63	18.23	19.37	21.19	22.79	22.56	20.74	18.69
V1	21.22	19.86	19.86	20.13	19.86	21.76	23.12	25.30	27.20	26.93	24.75	22.30
V2	17.28	16.17	16.17	16.40	16.17	17.73	18.83	20.61	22.16	21.94	20.16	18.17

H = 5.0   VB = 20.0   ALT = 0.0

Wind direction

	0	30	60	90	120	150	180	210	240	270	300	330
DS	100.00	100.00	100.00	100.00	100.00	100.00	100.00	100.00	100.00	100.00	100.00	100.00
DT	15.00	15.00	15.00	15.00	15.00	15.00	15.00	15.00	15.00	15.00	15.00	15.00
VE	19.84	18.57	18.57	18.82	18.57	20.35	21.62	23.66	25.44	25.18	23.15	20.86
VI	15.24	14.26	14.26	14.45	14.26	15.63	16.60	18.17	19.53	19.34	17.77	16.02
VO	16.92	15.84	15.84	16.06	15.84	17.36	18.44	20.18	21.70	21.48	19.74	17.79
V1	21.22	19.86	19.86	20.13	19.86	21.76	23.12	25.30	27.20	26.93	24.75	22.30
V2	17.28	16.17	16.17	16.40	16.17	17.73	18.83	20.61	22.16	21.94	20.16	18.17

Inland town: effect of town size
Diagonals 'a' 5 m, 200 m, 50 m.
H = 5.0   VB = 20.0   ALT = 0.0

Wind direction

	0	30	60	90	120	150	180	210	240	270	300	330
DS	100.00	100.00	100.00	100.00	100.00	100.00	100.00	100.00	100.00	100.00	100.00	100.00
DT	0.30	0.30	0.30	0.30	0.30	0.30	0.30	0.30	0.30	0.30	0.30	0.30
VE	27.49	25.73	25.73	26.08	25.73	28.20	29.96	32.78	35.25	34.90	32.08	28.90
VI	23.01	21.54	21.54	21.83	21.54	23.60	25.08	27.44	29.50	29.21	26.85	24.19
VO	24.75	23.16	23.16	23.48	23.16	25.38	26.97	29.51	31.73	31.41	28.88	26.02
V1	27.61	25.84	25.84	26.20	25.84	28.32	30.09	32.92	35.40	35.05	32.21	29.03
V2	23.55	22.04	22.04	22.35	22.04	24.16	25.67	28.08	30.20	29.90	27.48	24.76

H = 20.0 VB = 20.0 ALT = 0.0

Wind direction

	0	30	60	90	120	150	180	210	240	270	300	330
DS	100.00	100.00	100.00	100.00	100.00	100.00	100.00	100.00	100.00	100.00	100.00	100.00
DT	1.80	1.80	1.80	1.80	1.80	1.80	1.80	1.80	1.80	1.80	1.80	1.80
VE	27.59	25.82	25.82	26.18	25.82	28.30	30.07	32.90	35.37	35.02	32.19	29.01
VI	22.58	21.14	21.14	21.43	21.14	23.16	24.61	26.93	28.95	28.66	26.35	23.74
VO	24.53	22.95	22.95	23.27	22.95	25.16	26.73	29.24	31.44	31.13	28.61	25.78
V1	27.61	25.84	25.84	26.20	25.84	28.32	30.09	32.92	35.40	35.05	32.21	29.03
V2	23.55	22.04	22.04	22.35	22.04	24.16	25.67	28.08	30.20	29.90	27.48	24.76

H = 20.0 VB = 20.0 ALT = 0.0

Wind direction

	0	30	60	90	120	150	180	210	240	270	300	330
DS	100.00	100.00	100.00	100.00	100.00	100.00	100.00	100.00	100.00	100.00	100.00	100.00
DT	2.50	2.50	2.50	2.50	2.50	2.50	2.50	2.50	2.50	2.50	2.50	2.50
VE	27.49	25.72	25.72	26.08	25.72	28.19	29.95	32.77	35.24	34.89	32.07	28.90
VI	22.45	21.02	21.02	21.30	21.02	23.03	24.47	26.77	28.79	28.50	26.20	23.61
VO	24.41	22.84	22.84	23.15	22.84	25.03	26.60	29.10	31.29	30.98	28.47	25.66
V1	27.61	25.84	25.84	26.20	25.84	28.32	30.09	32.92	35.40	35.05	32.21	29.03
V2	23.55	22.04	22.04	22.35	22.04	24.16	25.67	28.08	30.20	29.90	27.48	24.76

H = 20.0 VB = 20.0 ALT = 0.0

Wind direction

	0	30	60	90	120	150	180	210	240	270	300	330
DS	100.00	100.00	100.00	100.00	100.00	100.00	100.00	100.00	100.00	100.00	100.00	100.00
DT	15.00	15.00	15.00	15.00	15.00	15.00	15.00	15.00	15.00	15.00	15.00	15.00
VE	26.29	24.61	24.61	24.94	24.61	26.97	28.65	31.35	33.71	33.37	30.67	27.64
VI	21.45	20.07	20.07	20.35	20.07	22.00	23.37	25.57	27.50	27.22	25.02	22.55
VO	23.32	21.83	21.83	22.13	21.83	23.92	25.42	27.81	29.90	29.60	27.21	24.52
V1	27.61	25.84	25.84	26.20	25.84	28.32	30.09	32.92	35.40	35.05	32.21	29.03
V2	23.55	22.04	22.04	22.35	22.04	24.16	25.67	28.08	30.20	29.90	27.48	24.76

Inland town: effect of town size
Diagonals 'a' 5 m, 200 m, 50 m.
H = 20.0 VB = 20.0 ALT = 0.0

Wind direction

	0	30	60	90	120	150	180	210	240	270	300	330
DS	100.00	100.00	100.00	100.00	100.00	100.00	100.00	100.00	100.00	100.00	100.00	100.00
DT	0.30	0.30	0.30	0.30	0.30	0.30	0.30	0.30	0.30	0.30	0.30	0.30
VE	31.92	29.87	29.87	30.28	29.87	32.74	34.78	38.06	40.92	40.51	37.24	33.56
VI	28.15	26.35	26.35	26.71	26.35	28.87	30.68	33.57	36.09	35.73	32.84	29.60
VO	29.76	27.85	27.85	28.23	27.85	30.52	32.43	35.48	38.15	37.77	34.72	31.28
V1	32.29	30.22	30.22	30.64	30.22	33.12	35.19	38.50	41.40	40.99	37.67	33.95
V2	27.55	25.78	25.78	26.13	25.78	28.25	30.02	32.84	35.32	34.96	32.14	28.96

H = 100.0   VB = 20.0   ALT = 0.0

Wind direction

	0	30	60	90	120	150	180	210	240	270	300	330
DS	100.00	100.00	100.00	100.00	100.00	100.00	100.00	100.00	100.00	100.00	100.00	100.00
DT	1.80	1.80	1.80	1.80	1.80	1.80	1.80	1.80	1.80	1.80	1.80	1.80
VE	32.00	29.95	29.95	30.36	29.95	32.82	34.87	38.15	41.03	40.62	37.33	33.64
VI	28.06	26.26	26.26	26.26	26.26	28.78	30.58	33.45	35.97	35.61	32.73	29.50
VO	29.74	27.83	27.83	28.21	27.83	30.50	32.41	35.46	38.13	37.74	34.69	31.26
V1	32.29	30.22	30.22	30.64	30.22	33.12	35.19	38.50	41.40	40.99	37.67	33.95
V2	27.55	25.78	25.78	26.13	25.78	28.25	30.02	32.84	35.32	34.96	32.14	28.96

H = 100.0   VB = 20.0   ALT = 0.0

Wind direction

	0	30	60	90	120	150	180	210	240	270	300	330
DS	100.00	100.00	100.00	100.00	100.00	100.00	100.00	100.00	100.00	100.00	100.00	100.00
DT	2.50	2.50	2.50	2.50	2.50	2.50	2.50	2.50	2.50	2.50	2.50	2.50
VE	32.06	30.00	30.00	30.42	30.00	32.88	34.94	38.22	41.10	40.69	37.40	33.70
VI	27.99	26.20	26.20	26.56	26.20	28.71	30.50	33.37	35.89	35.53	32.66	29.43
VO	29.72	27.82	27.82	28.20	27.82	30.49	32.39	35.44	38.11	37.73	34.68	31.25
V1	32.29	30.22	30.22	30.64	30.22	33.12	35.19	38.50	41.40	40.99	37.67	33.95
V2	27.55	25.78	25.78	26.13	25.78	28.25	30.02	32.84	35.32	34.96	32.14	28.96

H = 100.0   VB = 20.0   ALT = 0.0

Wind direction

	0	30	60	90	120	150	180	210	240	270	300	330
DS	100.00	100.00	100.00	100.00	100.00	100.00	100.00	100.00	100.00	100.00	100.00	100.00
DT	15.00	15.00	15.00	15.00	15.00	15.00	15.00	15.00	15.00	15.00	15.00	15.00
VE	32.40	30.32	30.32	30.74	30.32	33.23	35.30	38.63	41.54	41.12	37.80	34.06
VI	27.81	26.03	26.03	26.39	26.03	28.53	30.31	33.16	35.66	35.30	32.45	29.24
VO	29.77	27.86	27.86	28.24	27.86	30.53	32.44	35.49	38.16	37.78	34.73	31.29
V1	32.29	30.22	30.22	30.64	30.22	33.12	35.19	38.50	41.40	40.99	37.67	33.95
V2	27.55	25.78	25.78	26.13	25.78	28.25	30.02	32.84	35.32	34.96	32.14	28.96

Inland town: effect of town size
Diagonals 'a' 5 m, 200 m, 50 m.
H = 100.0   VB = 20.0   ALT = 0.0

Wind direction

	0	30	60	90	120	150	180	210	240	270	300	330
DS	100.00	100.00	100.00	100.00	100.00	75.00	20.00	1.50	0.30	1.50	15.00	80.00
DT	1.00	2.20	3.00	2.20	1.00	0.50	0.30	0.20	0.20	0.20	0.30	0.50
VE	21.54	19.58	19.39	19.85	20.16	23.06	26.01	30.03	32.35	31.97	27.96	23.56
VI	16.54	15.04	14.89	15.25	15.48	17.71	20.03	23.22	25.29	24.72	21.53	18.10
VO	18.38	16.71	16.54	16.93	17.20	19.67	22.22	25.72	27.88	27.38	23.88	20.10
V1	22.62	19.86	19.86	20.13	21.17	23.46	26.15	30.24	32.95	32.20	28.25	23.99
V2	19.30	16.17	16.17	16.40	18.06	20.02	22.31	26.64	29.02	28.36	24.10	20.46

H = 5.0   VB = 20.0   ALT = 0.0

Wind direction

	0	30	60	90	120	150	180	210	240	270	300	330
DS	1.50	15.00	80.00	100.00	100.00	100.00	100.00	100.00	75.00	20.00	1.50	0.30
DT	0.20	0.30	0.50	1.00	2.20	3.00	2.20	1.00	0.50	0.30	0.20	0.20
VE	25.19	22.43	20.98	20.44	19.58	21.25	22.80	25.69	28.83	30.30	29.38	26.53
VI	19.48	17.27	16.11	15.69	15.04	16.31	17.51	19.72	22.14	23.33	22.73	20.74
VO	21.57	19.16	17.89	17.43	16.71	18.12	19.45	21.91	24.59	25.88	25.17	22.86
V1	25.37	22.66	21.36	21.46	19.86	21.76	23.12	26.97	29.33	30.46	29.59	27.02
V2	22.34	19.33	18.22	18.31	16.17	17.73	18.83	23.01	25.02	25.98	26.06	23.79

H = 5.0   VB = 20.0   ALT = 0.0

Wind direction

	0	30	60	90	120	150	180	210	240	270	300	330
DS	20.00	1.50	0.30	1.50	15.00	80.00	100.00	100.00	100.00	100.00	100.00	75.00
DT	0.30	0.20	0.20	0.20	0.30	0.50	1.00	2.20	3.00	2.20	1.00	0.50
VE	23.87	23.57	23.62	23.89	22.43	22.99	23.48	24.95	26.56	22.56	25.13	23.64
VI	18.38	18.23	18.46	18.48	17.27	17.65	18.03	19.16	20.39	20.40	19.30	18.15
VO	20.39	20.19	20.35	20.46	19.16	19.61	20.03	21.28	22.65	22.66	21.44	20.16
V1	24.00	23.74	24.05	24.06	22.66	23.41	24.65	25.30	27.20	26.93	26.39	24.05
V2	20.47	20.91	21.18	21.20	19.33	19.97	21.03	20.61	22.16	21.94	22.51	20.52

H = 5.0   VB = 20.0   ALT = 0.0

Wind direction

	0	30	60	90	120	150	180	210	240	270	300	330
DS	100.00	100.00	75.00	20.00	1.50	0.30	1.50	15.00	80.00	100.00	100.00	100.00
DT	2.20	1.00	0.50	0.30	0.20	0.20	0.20	0.30	0.50	1.00	2.20	3.00
VE	20.92	20.16	21.04	22.65	23.57	25.88	27.45	28.57	28.74	27.34	24.41	21.78
VI	16.07	15.48	16.16	17.44	18.23	20.23	21.23	22.00	22.07	21.00	18.75	16.72
VO	17.85	17.20	17.95	19.35	20.19	22.30	23.51	24.41	24.51	23.32	20.82	18.58
V1	21.22	21.17	21.41	22.77	23.74	26.36	27.64	28.87	29.26	28.71	24.75	22.30
V2	17.28	18.06	18.26	19.42	20.91	23.21	24.35	24.63	24.96	24.49	20.16	18.17

Small coastal town; site close to sea.

Diagonals 'a' 5 m, 200 m, 50 m.

H = 5.0   VB = 20.0   ALT = 0.0

Wind direction

	0	30	60	90	120	150	180	210	240	270	300	330
DS	100.00	100.00	100.00	100.00	100.00	75.00	20.00	1.50	0.30	1.50	15.00	80.00
DT	1.00	2.20	3.00	2.20	1.00	0.50	0.30	0.20	0.20	0.20	0.30	0.50
VE	27.66	25.77	25.64	26.12	25.89	28.67	31.66	34.90	37.51	37.15	34.01	29.31
VI	22.76	21.07	20.94	21.35	21.30	23.82	26.54	29.74	32.41	31.66	28.51	24.34
VO	24.66	22.89	22.76	23.20	23.08	25.70	28.52	31.74	34.38	33.79	30.65	26.27
V1	27.61	25.84	25.84	26.20	25.84	28.62	31.71	35.33	37.95	37.61	34.16	29.27
V2	23.55	22.04	22.04	22.35	22.04	24.41	27.05	31.11	33.42	33.12	29.14	24.97

H = 20.0   VB = 20.0   ALT = 0.0

Wind direction

	0	30	60	90	120	150	180	210	240	270	300	330
DS	1.50	15.00	80.00	100.00	100.00	100.00	100.00	100.00	75.00	20.00	1.50	0.30
DT	0.20	0.30	0.50	1.00	2.20	3.00	2.20	1.00	0.50	0.30	0.20	0.20
VE	29.27	27.28	26.09	26.24	25.77	28.10	30.01	32.98	35.84	36.87	34.15	30.76
VI	24.94	22.87	21.67	21.59	21.07	22.94	24.53	27.14	29.78	30.91	29.10	26.57
VO	26.62	24.58	23.39	23.39	22.89	24.94	26.65	29.40	32.13	33.22	31.06	28.20
V1	29.63	27.41	26.06	26.20	25.84	28.32	30.09	32.92	35.78	36.93	34.57	31.12
V2	26.10	23.38	22.23	22.35	22.04	24.16	25.67	28.08	30.52	31.50	30.45	27.41

H = 20.0   VB = 20.0   ALT = 0.0

Wind direction

	0	30	60	90	120	150	180	210	240	270	300	330
DS	20.00	1.50	0.30	1.50	15.00	80.00	100.00	100.00	100.00	100.00	100.00	75.00
DT	0.30	0.20	0.20	0.20	0.30	0.50	1.00	2.20	3.00	2.20	1.00	0.50
VE	29.05	27.39	27.38	27.77	27.28	28.59	30.14	32.83	35.13	34.95	32.27	29.39
VI	24.35	23.34	23.66	23.66	22.87	23.75	24.80	26.84	28.68	28.57	26.55	24.42
VO	26.17	24.91	25.10	25.26	24.58	25.63	26.87	29.16	31.18	31.04	28.77	26.35
V1	29.10	27.73	27.70	28.11	27.41	28.55	30.09	32.92	35.40	35.05	32.21	29.34
V2	24.82	24.42	24.40	24.76	23.38	24.36	25.67	28.08	30.20	29.90	27.48	25.03

H = 20.0   VB = 20.0   ALT = 0.0

Wind direction

	0	30	60	90	120	150	180	210	240	270	300	330
DS	100.00	100.00	75.00	20.00	1.50	0.30	1.50	15.00	80.00	100.00	100.00	100.00
DT	2.20	1.00	0.50	0.30	0.20	0.20	0.20	0.30	0.50	1.00	2.20	3.00
VE	27.53	25.89	26.17	27.56	27.39	30.01	31.90	34.76	35.74	35.11	32.12	28.81
VI	22.51	21.30	21.74	23.10	23.34	25.92	27.18	29.14	29.69	28.89	26.26	23.52
VO	24.46	23.08	23.45	24.83	24.91	27.51	29.01	31.32	32.03	31.30	28.53	25.57
V1	27.61	25.84	26.12	27.60	27.73	30.36	32.29	34.92	35.69	35.05	32.21	29.03
V2	23.55	22.04	22.28	23.55	24.42	26.74	28.44	29.78	30.45	29.90	27.48	24.76

Small coastal town; site close to sea.
Diagonals 'a' 5 m, 200 m, 50 m.
H = 20.0   VB = 20.0   ALT = 0.0

Wind direction

	0	30	60	90	120	150	180	210	240	270	300	330
DS	100.00	100.00	100.00	100.00	100.00	75.00	20.00	4.00	3.00	4.00	20.00	80.00
DT	0.30	0.30	0.20	0.20	0.30	0.50	1.00	2.20	3.00	2.20	1.00	0.50
VE	22.50	21.06	21.14	21.43	21.06	23.06	24.91	27.14	29.09	28.89	26.67	23.56
VI	17.32	16.21	16.36	16.59	16.21	17.71	19.13	20.84	22.34	22.19	20.48	18.10
VO	19.22	17.99	18.12	18.36	17.99	19.67	21.25	23.15	24.81	24.64	22.75	20.10
V1	22.62	21.17	21.17	21.46	21.17	23.46	26.15	27.52	29.76	29.29	29.00	23.99
V2	19.30	18.06	18.06	18.31	18.06	20.02	22.31	22.42	22.24	23.86	23.88	20.46

H = 5.0 VB = 20.0 ALT = 0.0

Wind direction

	0	30	60	90	120	150	180	210	240	270	300	330
DS	4.00	20.00	80.00	100.00	100.00	100.00	100.00	100.00	75.00	20.00	4.00	3.00
DT	2.20	1.00	0.50	0.30	0.30	0.20	0.20	0.30	0.50	1.00	2.20	3.00
VE	22.76	21.39	20.98	21.34	21.06	23.17	24.62	26.82	28.83	29.01	26.55	23.85
VI	17.48	16.43	16.11	16.43	16.21	17.93	19.05	20.65	22.14	22.28	20.40	18.32
VO	19.42	18.25	17.89	18.23	17.99	19.85	21.09	22.92	24.59	24.75	22.65	20.34
V1	23.08	22.46	21.36	21.46	21.17	23.20	24.65	26.97	29.33	30.46	26.93	24.40
V2	18.80	19.16	18.22	18.31	18.06	19.79	21.03	23.01	25.02	25.98	21.93	19.88

H = 5.0 VB = 20.0 ALT = 0.0

Wind direction

	0	30	60	90	120	150	180	210	240	270	300	330
DS	20.00	4.00	3.00	4.00	20.00	80.00	100.00	100.00	100.00	100.00	100.00	75.00
DT	1.00	2.20	3.00	2.20	1.00	0.50	0.30	0.30	0.20	0.20	0.30	0.50
VE	22.86	21.30	21.23	21.59	21.39	22.99	24.52	26.82	28.96	28.68	26.25	23.64
VI	17.55	16.36	16.31	16.59	16.43	17.65	18.88	20.65	22.42	22.19	20.21	18.15
VO	19.50	18.17	18.11	18.42	18.25	19.61	20.95	22.92	24.82	24.57	22.42	20.16
V1	24.00	21.60	21.73	21.90	22.46	23.41	24.65	26.97	29.00	28.71	26.39	24.05
V2	20.47	17.60	17.70	17.84	19.16	19.97	21.03	23.01	24.74	24.49	22.51	20.52

H = 5.0 VB = 20.0 ALT = 0.0

Wind direction

	0	30	60	90	120	150	180	210	240	270	300	330
DS	100.00	100.00	75.00	20.00	4.00	3.00	4.00	20.00	80.00	100.00	100.00	100.00
DT	0.20	0.30	0.50	1.00	2.20	3.00	2.20	1.00	0.50	0.30	0.30	0.20
VE	22.59	21.06	21.04	21.69	21.30	23.27	24.80	27.25	28.74	28.56	26.25	23.75
VI	17.48	16.21	16.16	16.65	16.36	17.87	19.05	20.93	22.07	21.99	20.21	18.38
VO	19.36	17.99	17.95	18.50	18.17	19.85	21.16	23.25	24.51	24.40	22.42	20.35
V1	22.62	21.17	21.41	22.77	21.60	23.81	25.15	28.61	29.26	28.71	26.39	23.78
V2	19.30	18.06	18.26	19.42	17.60	19.40	20.49	24.41	24.96	24.49	22.51	20.28

Small coastal town; site away from sea.

Diagonals 'a' 5 m, 200 m, 50 m.

H = 5.0 VB = 20.0 ALT = 0.0

Wind direction

	0	30	60	90	120	150	180	210	240	270	300	330
DS	100.00	100.00	100.00	100.00	100.00	75.00	20.00	4.00	3.00	4.00	20.00	80.00
DT	0.30	0.30	0.20	0.20	0.30	0.50	1.00	2.20	3.00	2.20	1.00	0.50
VE	27.49	25.73	25.65	26.01	25.73	28.67	31.83	34.88	37.30	37.13	34.08	29.31
VI	23.01	21.54	21.61	21.91	21.54	23.82	26.24	28.66	30.66	30.51	28.09	24.34
VO	24.75	23.16	23.18	23.50	23.16	25.70	28.41	31.07	33.24	33.08	30.41	26.27
V1	27.61	25.84	25.84	26.20	25.84	28.62	31.71	35.36	38.02	37.64	33.94	29.27
V2	23.55	22.04	22.04	22.35	22.04	24.41	27.05	31.14	33.48	33.15	28.96	24.97

H = 20.0   VB = 20.0   ALT = 0.0

Wind direction

	0	30	60	90	120	150	180	210	240	270	300	330
DS	4.00	20.00	80.00	100.00	100.00	100.00	100.00	100.00	75.00	20.00	4.00	3.00
DT	2.20	1.00	0.50	0.30	0.30	0.20	0.20	0.30	0.50	1.00	2.20	3.00
VE	29.25	27.34	26.09	26.08	25.73	28.11	29.87	32.78	35.84	37.07	34.13	30.59
VI	24.04	22.53	21.67	21.83	21.54	23.68	25.16	27.44	29.78	30.56	28.04	25.14
VO	26.06	24.40	23.39	23.48	23.16	25.40	26.99	29.51	32.13	33.08	30.40	27.25
V1	29.65	27.23	26.06	26.20	25.84	28.32	30.09	32.92	35.78	36.93	34.60	31.17
V2	26.12	23.23	22.23	22.35	22.04	24.16	25.67	28.08	30.52	31.50	30.47	27.46

H = 20.0   VB = 20.0   ALT = 0.0

Wind direction

	0	30	60	90	120	150	180	210	240	270	300	330
DS	20.00	4.00	3.00	4.00	20.00	80.00	100.00	100.00	100.00	100.00	100.00	75.00
DT	1.00	2.20	3.00	2.20	1.00	0.50	0.30	0.30	0.20	0.20	0.30	0.50
VE	29.21	27.38	27.23	27.75	27.34	28.59	29.96	32.78	35.14	34.79	32.08	29.39
VI	24.07	22.50	22.38	22.80	22.53	23.75	25.08	27.44	29.61	29.31	26.85	24.42
VO	26.07	24.39	24.26	24.72	24.40	25.63	26.97	29.51	31.75	31.44	28.88	26.35
V1	29.10	27.75	27.75	28.13	27.23	28.55	30.09	32.92	35.40	35.05	32.21	29.34
V2	24.82	24.44	24.44	24.78	23.23	24.36	25.67	28.08	30.20	29.90	27.48	25.03

H = 20.0   VB = 20.0   ALT = 0.0

Wind direction

	0	30	60	90	120	150	180	210	240	270	300	330
DS	100.00	100.00	75.00	20.00	4.00	3.00	4.00	20.00	80.00	100.00	100.00	100.00
DT	0.20	0.30	0.50	1.00	2.20	3.00	2.20	1.00	0.50	0.30	0.30	0.20
VE	27.41	25.73	26.17	27.71	27.38	29.84	31.88	34.83	35.74	34.90	32.08	28.82
VI	23.09	21.54	21.74	22.84	22.50	24.53	26.19	28.70	29.69	29.21	26.85	24.28
VO	24.77	23.16	23.45	24.73	24.39	26.59	28.40	31.08	32.03	31.41	28.88	26.04
V1	27.61	25.84	26.12	27.60	27.75	30.41	32.31	34.69	35.69	35.05	32.21	29.03
V2	23.55	22.04	22.28	23.55	24.44	26.79	28.46	29.59	30.45	29.90	27.48	24.76

Small coastal town; site away from sea.

Diagonals 'a' 5 m, 200 m, 50 m.

H = 20.0   VB = 20.0   ALT = 0.0

Wind direction

	0	30	60	90	120	150	180	210	240	270	300	330
DS	100.00	100.00	100.00	100.00	100.00	75.00	20.00	1.50	0.30	1.50	15.00	80.00
DT	5.00	11.00	15.00	11.00	5.00	2.50	1.50	1.00	0.30	1.00	1.50	2.50
VE	20.40	18.70	18.57	18.96	19.09	21.68	24.52	28.64	32.20	30.48	26.35	22.15
VI	15.66	14.36	14.26	14.56	14.66	16.65	18.83	21.98	25.04	23.39	20.24	17.01
VO	17.40	15.95	15.84	16.17	16.29	18.49	20.92	24.42	27.67	25.99	22.48	18.90
V1	21.22	19.86	19.86	20.13	19.86	21.95	26.15	30.24	32.95	32.20	28.25	22.46
V2	17.28	16.17	16.17	16.40	16.17	17.88	22.31	26.64	29.02	28.36	24.10	18.29

H = 5.0 VB = 20.0 ALT = 0.0

Wind direction

	0	30	60	90	120	150	180	210	240	270	300	330
DS	1.50	15.00	80.00	100.00	100.00	100.00	100.00	100.00	75.00	20.00	1.50	0.30
DT	1.00	1.50	2.50	5.00	11.00	15.00	11.00	5.00	2.50	1.50	1.00	0.30
VE	24.02	21.14	19.72	19.35	18.70	20.35	21.78	24.32	27.10	28.56	28.02	26.40
VI	18.43	16.24	15.14	14.86	14.36	15.63	16.72	18.68	20.81	21.93	21.50	20.54
VO	20.48	18.03	16.82	16.51	15.95	17.36	18.58	20.75	23.12	24.36	23.89	22.69
V1	25.37	22.66	19.99	20.13	19.86	21.76	23.12	25.30	27.44	30.46	29.59	27.02
V2	22.34	19.33	16.28	16.40	16.17	17.73	18.83	20.61	22.35	25.98	26.06	23.79

H = 5.0 VB = 20.0 ALT = 0.0

Wind direction

	0	30	60	90	120	150	180	210	240	270	300	330
DS	20.00	1.50	0.30	1.50	15.00	80.00	100.00	100.00	100.00	100.00	100.00	75.00
DT	1.50	1.00	0.30	1.00	1.50	2.50	5.00	11.00	15.00	11.00	5.00	2.50
VE	22.50	22.48	23.50	22.79	21.14	21.61	22.23	23.83	25.44	25.36	23.80	22.22
VI	17.28	17.25	18.28	17.49	16.24	16.60	17.07	18.30	19.53	19.48	18.28	17.07
VO	19.19	19.17	20.20	19.43	18.03	18.44	18.96	20.32	21.70	21.63	20.30	18.96
V1	24.00	23.74	24.05	24.06	22.66	21.91	23.12	25.30	27.20	26.93	24.75	22.50
V2	20.47	20.91	21.18	21.20	19.33	17.85	18.83	20.61	22.16	21.94	20.16	18.33

H = 5.0 VB = 20.0 ALT = 0.0

Wind direction

	0	30	60	90	120	150	180	210	240	270	300	330
DS	100.00	100.00	75.00	20.00	1.50	0.30	1.50	15.00	80.00	100.00	100.00	100.00
DT	11.00	5.00	2.50	1.50	1.00	0.30	1.00	1.50	2.50	5.00	11.00	15.00
VE	19.98	19.09	19.78	21.35	22.48	25.76	26.17	26.93	27.01	25.89	23.31	20.86
VI	15.35	14.66	15.19	16.39	17.25	20.03	20.09	20.68	20.75	19.88	17.90	16.02
VO	17.05	16.29	16.88	18.21	19.17	22.13	22.32	22.98	23.04	22.09	19.89	17.79
V1	21.22	19.86	20.03	22.77	23.74	26.36	27.64	28.87	27.38	26.93	24.75	22.30
V2	17.28	16.17	16.32	19.42	20.91	23.21	24.35	24.63	22.31	21.94	20.16	18.17

Large coastal town; site close to sea.

Diagonals 'a' 5 m, 200 m, 50 m.

H = 5.0 VB = 20.0 ALT = 0.0

Wind direction

	0	30	60	90	120	150	180	210	240	270	300	330
DS	100.00	100.00	100.00	100.00	100.00	75.00	20.00	1.50	0.30	1.50	15.00	80.00
DT	5.00	11.00	15.00	11.00	5.00	2.50	1.50	1.00	0.30	1.00	1.50	2.50
VE	27.07	24.79	24.61	25.13	25.34	28.56	31.79	35.04	37.51	37.30	34.15	29.19
VI	22.08	20.22	20.07	20.50	20.66	23.34	26.10	29.19	32.21	31.07	28.04	23.85
VO	24.01	21.99	21.83	22.29	22.48	25.37	28.31	31.46	34.27	33.49	30.41	25.92
V1	27.61	25.84	25.84	26.20	25.84	28.62	31.71	35.33	37.95	37.61	34.16	29.27
V2	23.55	22.04	22.04	22.35	22.04	24.41	27.05	31.11	33.42	33.12	29.14	24.97

H = 20.0   VB = 20.0   ALT = 0.0

Wind direction

	0	30	60	90	120	150	180	210	240	270	300	330
DS	1.50	15.00	80.00	100.00	100.00	100.00	100.00	100.00	75.00	20.00	1.50	0.30
DT	1.00	1.50	2.50	5.00	11.00	15.00	11.00	5.00	2.50	1.50	1.00	0.30
VE	29.39	27.40	25.99	25.68	24.79	26.97	28.86	32.28	35.70	37.03	34.29	30.76
VI	24.48	22.50	21.24	20.95	20.22	22.00	23.54	26.33	29.18	30.40	28.56	26.42
VO	26.39	24.40	23.08	22.78	21.99	23.92	25.61	28.63	31.71	32.97	30.78	28.10
V1	29.63	27.41	26.06	26.20	25.84	28.32	30.09	32.92	35.78	36.93	34.57	31.12
V2	26.10	23.38	22.23	22.35	22.04	24.16	25.67	28.08	30.52	31.50	30.45	27.41

H = 20.0   VB = 20.0   ALT = 0.0

Wind direction

	0	30	60	90	120	150	180	210	240	270	300	330
DS	20.00	1.50	0.30	1.50	15.00	80.00	100.00	100.00	100.00	100.00	100.00	75.00
DT	1.50	1.00	0.30	1.00	1.50	2.50	5.00	11.00	5.00	11.00	5.00	2.50
VE	29.17	27.51	27.38	27.88	27.40	28.48	29.50	31.58	33.71	33.62	31.58	29.27
VI	23.95	22.91	23.52	23.23	22.50	23.27	24.06	25.76	27.50	27.42	25.76	23.93
VO	25.98	24.69	25.02	25.03	24.40	25.29	26.17	28.02	29.90	29.82	28.02	26.00
V1	29.10	27.73	27.70	28.11	27.41	28.55	30.09	32.92	35.40	35.05	32.21	29.34
V2	24.82	24.42	24.40	24.76	23.38	24.36	25.67	28.08	30.20	29.90	27.48	25.03

H = 20.0   VB = 20.0   ALT = 0.0

Wind direction

	0	30	60	90	120	150	180	210	240	270	300	330
DS	100.00	100.00	75.00	20.00	1.50	0.30	1.50	15.00	80.00	100.00	100.00	100.00
DT	11.00	5.00	2.50	1.50	1.00	0.30	1.00	1.50	2.50	5.00	1.00	15.00
VE	26.49	25.34	26.06	27.68	27.51	30.01	32.03	34.90	35.60	34.36	30.90	27.64
VI	21.61	20.66	21.30	22.72	22.91	25.77	26.68	28.66	29.09	28.02	25.21	22.55
VO	23.50	22.48	23.15	24.65	24.69	27.42	28.75	31.08	31.61	30.48	27.41	24.52
V1	27.61	25.84	26.12	27.60	27.73	30.36	32.29	34.92	35.69	35.05	32.21	29.03
V2	23.55	22.04	22.28	23.55	24.42	26.74	28.44	29.78	30.45	29.90	27.48	24.76

Large coastal town; site close to sea.
Diagonals 'a' 5 m, 200 m, 50 m.
H = 20.0   VB = 20.0   ALT = 0.0

Wind direction

	0	30	60	90	120	150	180	210	240	270	300	330
DS	100.00	100.00	100.00	100.00	100.00	75.00	20.00	13.00	15.00	16.00	20.00	80.00
DT	1.50	1.00	0.50	1.00	1.50	2.50	5.00	11.00	15.00	11.00	5.00	2.50
VE	21.21	20.16	20.74	20.44	19.85	21.68	23.59	25.42	27.09	26.99	25.25	22.15
VI	16.29	15.48	15.93	15.69	15.24	16.65	18.11	19.52	20.80	20.73	19.39	17.01
VO	18.09	17.20	17.69	17.43	16.93	18.49	20.12	21.68	23.11	23.03	21.54	18.90
V1	22.62	21.17	21.17	21.46	21.17	21.95	24.22	26.80	28.71	28.38	25.93	22.46
V2	19.30	18.06	18.06	18.31	18.06	17.88	19.73	21.83	23.39	23.12	21.12	18.29

H = 5.0   VB = 20.0   ALT = 0.0

Wind direction

	0	30	60	90	120	150	180	210	240	270	300	330
DS	16.00	20.00	80.00	100.00	100.00	100.00	100.00	100.00	75.00	20.00	13.00	15.00
DT	11.00	5.00	2.50	1.50	1.00	0.50	1.00	1.50	2.50	5.00	11.00	15.00
VE	21.27	20.26	19.72	20.12	20.16	22.73	23.48	25.29	27.10	27.47	24.87	22.22
VI	16.33	15.55	15.14	15.45	15.48	17.46	18.03	19.42	20.81	21.09	19.10	17.06
VO	18.14	17.28	16.82	17.16	17.20	19.39	20.03	21.57	23.12	23.43	21.22	18.95
V1	22.36	20.80	19.99	21.46	21.17	23.20	24.65	26.97	27.44	28.21	26.22	23.54
V2	18.21	16.95	16.28	18.31	18.06	19.79	21.03	23.01	22.35	22.98	21.36	19.18

H = 5.0   VB = 20.0   ALT = 0.0

Wind direction

	0	30	60	90	120	150	180	210	240	270	300	330
DS	20.00	13.00	15.00	16.00	20.00	80.00	100.00	100.00	100.00	100.00	100.00	75.00
DT	5.00	11.00	15.00	11.00	5.00	2.50	1.50	1.00	0.50	1.00	1.50	2.50
VE	21.64	19.95	19.78	20.18	20.26	21.61	23.11	25.69	28.41	27.34	24.74	22.22
VI	16.62	15.32	15.19	15.49	15.55	16.60	17.75	19.72	21.82	21.00	19.00	17.07
VO	18.46	17.02	16.87	17.21	17.28	18.44	19.71	21.91	24.24	23.32	21.11	18.96
V1	22.23	21.04	20.96	21.21	20.80	21.91	24.65	26.97	29.00	28.71	26.39	22.50
V2	18.11	17.14	17.07	17.28	16.95	17.85	21.03	23.01	24.74	24.49	22.51	18.33

H = 5.0   VB = 20.0   ALT = 0.0

Wind direction

	0	30	60	90	120	150	180	210	240	270	300	330
DS	100.00	100.00	75.00	20.00	13.00	15.00	16.00	20.00	80.00	100.00	100.00	100.00
DT	1.00	1.50	2.50	5.00	11.00	15.00	11.00	5.00	2.50	1.50	1.00	0.50
VE	21.54	19.85	19.78	20.53	19.95	21.67	23.18	25.81	27.01	26.92	25.13	23.30
VI	16.54	15.24	15.19	15.77	15.32	16.64	17.80	19.82	20.75	20.67	19.30	17.89
VO	18.38	16.93	16.88	17.51	17.02	18.49	19.77	22.01	23.04	22.96	21.44	19.88
V1	22.62	21.17	20.03	21.09	21.04	22.97	24.36	26.50	27.38	28.71	26.39	23.78
V2	19.30	18.06	16.32	17.18	17.14	18.71	19.85	21.59	22.31	24.49	22.51	20.28

Large coastal town; site away from the sea.

Diagonals 'a' 5 m, 200 m, 50 m.

H = 5.0   VB = 20.0   ALT = 0.0

Wind direction

	0	30	60	90	120	150	180	210	240	270	300	330
DS	100.00	100.00	100.00	100.00	100.00	75.00	20.00	13.00	15.00	16.00	20.00	80.00
DT	1.50	1.00	0.50	1.00	1.50	2.50	5.00	11.00	15.00	11.00	5.00	2.50
VE	27.63	25.89	25.82	26.24	25.86	28.56	31.15	33.50	35.71	35.59	33.35	29.19
VI	22.64	21.30	21.44	21.59	21.19	23.34	25.45	27.37	29.18	29.09	27.24	23.85
VO	24.58	23.08	23.14	23.39	23.00	25.37	27.66	29.75	31.71	31.61	29.61	25.92
V1	27.61	25.84	25.84	26.20	25.84	28.62	31.71	35.01	37.54	37.12	33.94	29.27
V2	23.55	22.04	22.04	22.35	22.04	24.41	27.05	29.87	32.03	31.66	28.96	24.97

H = 20.0   VB = 20.0   ALT = 0.0

Wind direction

	0	30	60	90	120	150	180	210	240	270	300	330
DS	16.00	20.00	80.00	100.00	100.00	100.00	100.00	100.00	75.00	20.00	13.00	15.00
DT	11.00	5.00	2.50	1.50	1.00	0.50	1.00	1.50	2.50	5.00	11.00	15.00
VE	28.04	26.75	25.99	26.21	25.89	28.30	30.14	32.94	35.70	36.28	32.78	29.28
VI	22.92	21.85	21.24	21.48	21.30	23.50	24.80	27.00	29.18	29.64	26.79	23.93
VO	24.90	23.75	23.08	23.32	23.08	25.36	26.87	29.30	31.71	32.21	29.11	26.01
V1	29.24	27.23	26.06	26.20	25.84	28.32	30.09	32.92	35.78	36.93	34.26	30.79
V2	24.95	23.23	22.23	22.35	22.04	24.16	25.67	28.08	30.52	31.50	29.22	26.26

H = 20.0   VB = 20.0   ALT = 0.0

Wind direction

	0	30	60	90	120	150	180	210	240	270	300	330
DS	20.00	13.00	15.00	16.00	20.00	80.00	100.00	100.00	100.00	100.00	100.00	75.00
DT	5.00	11.00	15.00	11.00	5.00	2.50	1.50	1.00	0.50	1.00	1.50	2.50
VE	28.58	26.29	26.07	26.61	26.75	28.48	30.11	32.98	35.38	35.11	32.23	29.27
VI	23.35	21.49	21.30	21.74	21.85	23.27	24.68	27.14	29.38	28.89	26.42	23.93
VO	25.38	23.35	23.15	23.63	23.75	25.29	26.78	29.40	31.70	31.30	28.67	26.00
V1	29.10	27.48	27.41	27.74	27.23	28.55	30.09	32.92	35.40	35.05	32.21	29.34
V2	24.82	23.44	23.38	23.67	23.23	24.36	25.67	28.08	30.20	29.90	27.48	25.03

H = 20.0   VB = 20.0   ALT = 0.0

Wind direction

	0	30	60	90	120	150	180	210	240	270	300	330
DS	100.00	100.00	75.00	20.00	13.00	15.00	16.00	20.00	80.00	100.00	100.00	100.00
DT	1.00	1.50	2.50	5.00	11.00	15.00	11.00	5.00	2.50	1.50	1.00	0.50
VE	27.66	25.86	26.06	27.12	26.29	28.57	30.56	34.08	35.60	35.07	32.27	29.01
VI	22.76	21.19	21.30	22.15	21.49	23.35	24.97	27.84	29.09	28.74	26.55	24.09
VO	24.66	23.00	23.15	24.08	23.35	25.37	27.14	30.26	31.61	31.19	28.77	26.00
V1	27.61	25.84	26.12	27.60	27.48	30.03	31.87	34.69	35.69	35.05	32.21	29.03
V2	23.55	22.04	22.28	23.55	23.44	25.62	27.19	29.59	30.45	29.90	27.48	24.76

Large coastal town; site away from the sea.
Diagonals 'a' 5 m, 200 m, 50 m.
H = 20.0   VB = 20.0   ALT = 0.0

Group 1. Section 3. Wind speed calculations

The third section of this group of examples is designed to help calibrate programs devised for the calculation of wind speeds, and gives values for all the separate factors employed in the derivation.

Across the top the label 'Wind direction' shows that the columns of values represent flow from that direction in degrees east of north.

The rows are then determined by the symbol in the left hand column.

DS   stands for distance from the sea.

DT   for distance into the town.

SC   is the value of the 'Fetch' factor S_c in the Directional method.

ST   is the value of the 'Turbulence' factor S_t in the Directional method.

TC   is the value of the 'Fetch Adjustment' factor T_c in the Directional method.

TT   is the value of the 'Turbulence Adjustment' Factor T_t in the Directional method.

GT   is the 'Gust Peak' factor for the first diagonal length 'a' in the Directional method.

GT   is the 'Gust Peak' factor for the second diagonal length 'a' in the Directional method.

SB   is the 'Terrain and Building' factor in the Standard method.

SH   is the 'Topography' factor in the Directional method.

VE   is the Wind Speed in m/s related to the first diagonal length 'a' in the Directional method. This is usually related to panel loads.

VI   is the Wind Speed in m/s related to the second diagonal length 'a' in the Directional method. This is usually related to internal volume.

VO   is the Wind Speed in m/s related to the third diagonal length 'a' in the Directional method. This is usually related to overall loads on the building.

V1   is the Wind Speed in m/s related to the first diagonal length 'a' in the Standard method. This is usually related to panel size (5 m).

V2   is the Wind Speed in m/s related to the second diagonal length 'a' in the Standard method. This is usually related to internal volume.

In the rubric are the following values

H   is the Effective Height in m.

a are the three values of diagonal length in m.

VB   is the Basic (Map) Wind Speed in m/s

ALT   is the Altitude in m above Sea Level.

The geography of the site used as an illustration here is interesting in that it accentuates the wind speeds around the south west in addition to the emphasis given to these directions by the directional factor. This situation is used in Group 2 Section 2 calculations.

Wind direction

	0	30	60	90	120	150	180	210	240	270	300	330
DS	100.00	100.00	100.00	100.00	100.00	75.00	20.00	1.50	0.30	1.50	15.00	80.00
DT	5.00	11.00	15.00	11.00	5.00	2.50	1.50	1.00	0.30	1.00	1.50	2.50
SC	0.882	0.882	0.882	0.882	0.882	0.895	0.936	0.981	1.020	0.981	0.939	0.892
ST	0.192	0.192	0.192	0.192	0.192	0.192	0.192	0.193	0.179	0.193	0.192	0.192
TC	0.714	0.699	0.694	0.699	0.714	0.729	0.743	0.754	0.795	0.754	0.743	0.729
TT	1.630	1.630	1.630	1.630	1.630	1.630	1.629	1.630	1.600	1.630	1.629	1.630
GT	3.44	3.44	3.44	3.44	3.44	3.44	3.44	3.44	3.44	3.44	3.44	3.44
GT	1.90	1.90	1.90	1.90	1.90	1.90	1.90	1.90	1.90	1.90	1.90	1.90
GT	2.46	2.46	2.46	2.46	2.46	2.46	2.46	2.46	2.46	2.46	2.46	2.46
SB	1.36	1.36	1.36	1.36	1.36	1.37	1.54	1.63	1.65	1.63	1.55	1.37
SH	0.000	0.000	0.000	0.000	0.000	0.000	0.000	0.000	0.000	0.000	0.000	0.000
VE	20.40	18.70	18.57	18.96	19.09	21.68	24.52	28.64	32.20	30.48	26.35	22.15
VI	15.66	14.36	14.26	14.56	14.66	16.65	18.83	21.98	25.04	23.39	20.24	17.01
VO	17.40	15.95	15.84	16.17	16.29	18.49	20.92	24.42	27.67	25.99	22.48	18.90
CE	1.00	1.00	1.00	1.00	1.00	1.00	1.00	1.00	1.00	1.00	1.00	1.00
CF	0.66	0.66	0.66	0.66	0.66	0.66	0.73	0.78	0.78	0.78	0.73	0.66
V1	21.22	19.86	19.86	20.13	19.86	21.95	26.15	30.24	32.95	32.20	28.25	22.46
V2	17.28	16.17	16.17	16.40	16.17	17.88	22.31	26.64	29.02	28.36	24.10	18.29

H = 5.0 a = 5.0, 200.0, 50.0   VB = 20.0   ALT = 0.0

Wind direction

	0	30	60	90	120	150	180	210	240	270	300	330
DS	100.00	100.00	100.00	100.00	100.00	75.00	20.00	1.50	0.30	1.50	15.00	80.00
DT	5.00	11.00	15.00	11.00	5.00	2.50	1.50	1.00	0.30	1.00	1.50	2.50
SC	1.130	1.130	1.130	1.130	1.130	1.147	1.200	1.254	1.310	1.254	1.205	1.143
ST	0.166	0.166	0.166	0.166	0.166	0.165	0.164	0.150	0.132	0.150	0.164	0.166
TC	0.840	0.822	0.816	0.822	0.840	0.858	0.873	0.886	0.935	0.886	0.873	0.858
TT	1.451	1.450	1.449	1.450	1.451	1.432	1.394	1.350	1.170	1.350	1.394	1.432
GT	3.44	3.44	3.44	3.44	3.44	3.44	3.44	3.44	3.44	3.44	3.44	3.44
GT	2.04	2.04	2.04	2.04	2.04	2.04	2.04	2.04	2.04	2.04	2.04	2.04
GT	2.58	2.58	2.58	2.58	2.58	2.58	2.58	2.58	2.58	2.58	2.58	2.58
SB	1.77	1.77	1.77	1.77	1.77	1.79	1.87	1.90	1.90	1.90	1.88	1.78
SH	0.000	0.000	0.000	0.000	0.000	0.000	0.000	0.000	0.000	0.000	0.000	0.000
VE	27.07	24.79	24.61	25.13	25.34	28.56	31.79	35.04	37.51	37.30	34.15	29.19
VI	22.08	20.22	20.07	20.50	20.66	23.34	26.10	29.19	32.21	31.07	28.04	23.85
VO	24.01	21.99	21.83	22.29	22.48	25.37	28.31	31.46	34.27	33.49	30.41	25.92
CE	1.00	1.00	1.00	1.00	1.00	1.00	1.00	1.00	1.00	1.00	1.00	1.00
CF	0.73	0.73	0.73	0.73	0.73	0.73	0.73	0.78	0.78	0.78	0.73	0.73
V1	27.61	25.84	25.84	26.20	25.84	28.62	31.71	35.33	37.95	37.61	34.16	29.27
V2	23.55	22.04	22.04	22.35	22.04	24.41	27.05	31.11	33.42	33.12	29.14	24.97

H = 20.0 a = 5.0, 200.0, 50.0   VB = 20.0   ALT = 0.0

Values of parameters
Standard distorted topography

Wind direction

	0	30	60	90	120	150	180	210	240	270	300	330
DS	100.00	100.00	100.00	100.00	100.00	75.00	20.00	1.50	0.30	1.50	15.00	80.00
DT	5.00	11.00	15.00	11.00	5.00	2.50	1.50	1.00	0.30	1.00	1.50	2.50
SC	1.130	1.130	1.130	1.130	1.130	1.147	1.200	1.254	1.310	1.254	1.205	1.143
ST	0.166	0.166	0.166	0.166	0.166	0.165	0.164	0.150	0.132	0.150	0.164	0.166
TC	0.840	0.822	0.816	0.822	0.840	0.858	0.873	0.886	0.935	0.886	0.873	0.858
TT	1.451	1.450	1.449	1.450	1.451	1.432	1.394	1.350	1.170	1.350	1.394	1.432
GT	3.44	3.44	3.44	3.44	3.44	3.44	3.44	3.44	3.44	3.44	3.44	3.44
GT	2.98	2.98	2.98	2.98	2.98	2.98	2.98	2.98	2.98	2.98	2.98	2.98
GT	2.58	2.58	2.58	2.58	2.58	2.58	2.58	2.58	2.58	2.58	2.58	2.58
SB	1.77	1.77	1.77	1.77	1.77	1.79	1.87	1.90	1.90	1.90	1.88	1.78
SH	0.000	0.000	0.000	0.000	0.000	0.000	0.000	0.000	0.000	0.000	0.000	0.000
VE	27.07	24.79	24.61	25.13	25.34	28.56	31.79	35.04	37.51	37.30	34.15	29.19
VI	25.43	23.29	23.12	23.61	23.80	26.85	29.92	33.12	35.77	35.26	32.15	27.44
VO	24.01	21.99	21.83	22.29	22.48	25.37	28.31	31.46	34.27	33.49	30.41	25.92
CE	1.00	1.00	1.00	1.00	1.00	1.00	1.00	1.00	1.00	1.00	1.00	1.00
CF	0.90	0.90	0.90	0.90	0.90	0.90	0.90	0.92	0.92	0.92	0.90	0.90
V1	27.61	25.84	25.84	26.20	25.84	28.62	31.71	35.33	37.95	37.61	34.16	29.27
V2	26.16	24.48	24.82	24.82	24.48	27.12	30.04	33.81	36.31	35.99	32.37	27.73

H = 20.0 a = 5.0, 20.0, 50.0   VB = 20.0   ALT = 0.0

Wind direction

	0	30	60	90	120	150	180	210	240	270	300	330
DS	100.00	100.00	100.00	100.00	100.00	75.00	20.00	1.50	0.30	1.50	15.00	80.00
DT	5.00	11.00	15.00	11.00	5.00	2.50	1.50	1.00	0.30	1.00	1.50	2.50
SC	1.130	1.130	1.130	1.130	1.130	1.147	1.200	1.254	1.310	1.254	1.205	1.143
ST	0.166	0.166	0.166	0.166	0.166	0.165	0.164	0.150	0.132	0.150	0.164	0.166
TC	0.840	0.822	0.816	0.822	0.840	0.858	0.873	0.886	0.935	0.886	0.873	0.858
TT	1.451	1.450	1.449	1.450	1.451	1.432	1.394	1.350	1.170	1.350	1.394	1.432
GT	3.44	3.44	3.44	3.44	3.44	3.44	3.44	3.44	3.44	3.44	3.44	3.44
GT	2.27	2.27	2.27	2.27	2.27	2.27	2.27	2.27	2.27	2.27	2.27	2.27
GT	2.04	2.04	2.04	2.04	2.04	2.04	2.04	2.04	2.04	2.04	2.04	2.04
SB	1.77	1.77	1.77	1.77	1.77	1.79	1.87	1.90	1.90	1.90	1.88	1.78
SH	0.000	0.000	0.000	0.000	0.000	0.000	0.000	0.000	0.000	0.000	0.000	0.000
VE	27.07	24.79	24.61	25.13	25.34	28.56	31.79	35.04	37.51	37.30	34.15	29.19
VI	22.90	20.97	20.82	21.26	21.43	24.20	27.04	30.15	33.09	32.10	29.05	24.73
VO	22.08	20.22	20.07	20.50	20.66	23.34	26.10	29.19	32.21	31.07	28.04	23.85
CE	1.00	1.00	1.00	1.00	1.00	1.00	1.00	1.00	1.00	1.00	1.00	1.00
CF	0.78	0.78	0.78	0.78	0.78	0.78	0.78	0.82	0.82	0.82	0.78	0.78
V1	27.61	25.84	25.84	26.20	25.84	28.62	31.71	35.33	37.95	37.61	34.16	29.27
V2	24.37	22.81	22.81	23.12	22.81	25.26	27.98	31.95	34.32	34.01	30.15	25.83

H = 20.0 a = 5.0, 100.0, 200.0,   VB = 20.0   ALT = 0.0

Values of parameters
Standard distorted topography

Group 2. Section 1. Pressure coefficient calculations

This section comprises a series of sheets used to derive average values of pressure coefficients for a selection of shapes. Each sheet is self-explanatory. They could be used as models of worksheets.

WD (°EON)	0	90
b (m)	40	10
A (m²)	80	5
B (m²)	80	5
C (m²)	240	40
D (m²)	–	350
Area Check (m²)	400	400
Av C_D	–1.10	–0.29

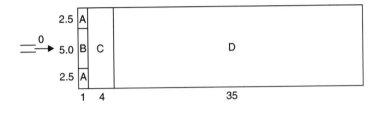

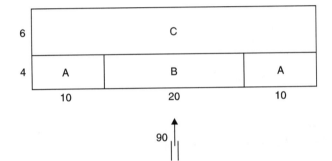

Values for **roof** pressure coefficients **flat rectangular roof** 40 m × 10 m × 20 m high. **Standard method** (Figure 6, Table 8)

WD (°EON)	0	30	60	90
b_W (m)	10	10	10	10
b_L (m)	40	40	40	40
A (m²)	8	8	8	8
B (m²)	24	24	24	24
C (m²)	40	40	40	40
D (m²)	80	80	80	80
E (m²)	118.5	118.5	118.5	118.5
F (m²)	120	120	120	120
G (m²)	–	–	–	–
H (m²)	0.5	0.5	0.5	0.5
I (m²)	–1.5	–1.5	–1.5	–1.5
J (m²)	7.5	7.5	7.5	7.5
AV C_D	–0.88	–0.91	–0.69	–0.45

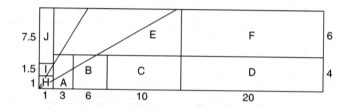

Values for **roof** pressure coefficients **flat rectangular roof** 40 m × 10 m × 20 m high. **Directional method simplified** (Figure 38, Table 34)

	area	area	area	area	area	area	area	area	area	area	area	area	area	area
WD	0		15		30		45		60		75		90	
Set	F	S	F	S	F	S	F	S	F	S	F	S	F	S
b	40		40		39.64		35.36		28.66		20.01		10.0	
A	16	–	14	2	11	5	6	16	2	6	–	4	–	2
B	24	–	24	11	23	21	19	19	11	12	3	6	–	3
C	40	–	40	–	39	–	31	4	21	8	9	10	–	3
D	80	–	80	–	80	–	79	–	74	–	60	–	–	5
E	120	–	109	–	95	3	70	21	25	58	1	61	–	20
F	120	–	120	–	122	–	144	–	180	–	140	–	–	20
G	–	–	–	–	–	–	–	–	–	3	–	100	–	350
Check	400		400		400		400		400		400		400	
AvC_D	-0.84		-0.91		-0.95		-0.80		-0.65		-0.35		-0.28	

For 'Set', F is front; S is side. All zones for 0° are front; all zones for 90° are side

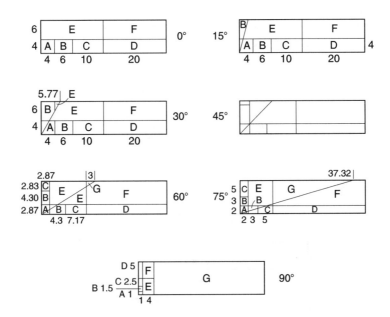

Values for **roof** pressure coefficients **flat rectangular roof** 40 m × 10 m × 20 m high. **Directional method full** (Figures 35 and 36, Table 30)

	WD	0		15		30		45		60		75		90	
Face	D/H	1.00		1.00		1.00		1.00		1.00		1.93		2.00	
	b	40.0		40.0		39.6		35.4		28.7		20.0		10.0	
		Ar	C_p	Ar	C_p	Ar	C_p	Ar	C_p	Ar	C_p	Ar	C_p	Ar	C_p
1	Theta	0		15		30		45		60		75		90	
	A	160	0.70	160	0.77	159	0.80	141	0.79	115	0.24	80	-1.10	40	-1.30
	B	640	0.83	640	0.88	634	0.80	566	0.69	459	0.51	320	-0.73	160	-1.00
	C	-	-	-	-	-	-	-	-	-	-	-	-	400	-0.42
	D	-	-	-	-	7	0.49	93	0.34	227	0.26	400	0.12	200	0.20
	C_p mean	0.80		0.86		0.80		0.67		0.40		-0.34		-0.49	
2	Theta	90		75		60		45		30		15		0	
	A	160	-1.30	160	-1.10	159	0.24	141	-79	115	0.80	80	-70	40	-63
	B	40	-1.00	40	-0.73	41	0.51	59	0.69	85	0.80	120	0.80	160	0.75
	C	-		-		-		-		-		-		-	
	D	-		-		-		-		-		-		-	
	C_p mean	-1.20		-1.03		0.30		0.76		0.80		0.76		0.73	
3	Theta	180		165		150		135		120		105		90	
	A	160	-0.34	160	-0.30	159	-0.34	141	-0.50	115	-0.63	80	-0.80	40	-1.30
	B	640	-1.24	640	-0.30	634	-0.34	566	-0.50	159	-0.63	320	-0.73	160	-0.80
	C	-		-		-		-		-		-		400	-0.42
	D	-		-		7	-0.32	93	-0.33	227	-0.29	400	-0.26	200	-0.20
	C_p mean	-0.26		-0.30		-0.34		-0.48		-0.53		-0.50		-0.49	
4	Theta	90		105		120		135		150		165		180	
	A	160	-1.30	160	-0.80	159	-0.63	141	-0.50	114	-0.34	80	-0.27	40	-0.28
	B	40	-0.80	40	-0.73	41	-0.63	59	-0.50	85	-0.34	120	-0.26	160	-0.21
	C	-		-		-		-		-		-		-	
	D	-		-		-		-		-		-		-	
	C_p mean	-1.24		0.79		-0.63		-0.50		-0.34		-0.26		0.22	

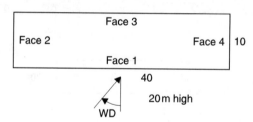

Pressure coefficients on **walls. Directional method** (Figure 31, Table 26)

	Front	Front	Rear	Rear	Side	Side
WD (°EON)	0	90	0	90	0	90
D/H	1	2	1	2		
b (m)					40	10
A (m^2)					160	40
B (m^2)					40	160
C (m^2)					–	600
Check Area (m^2)					200	800
Mean C$_p$	0.80	0.73	–0.30	–0.23	–1.20	–0.53

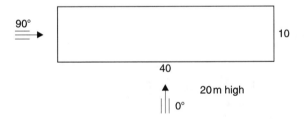

Pressure coefficients on **walls. Standard method** (Figure 9, Table 5)

| WD | | 0° | | | 90° | |
Face	b	D/H	C_p	b	D/H	C_p
1	10	1.5	0.77	30	2.5	−0.40
2	10	1.5	−0.90	30	2.5	−0.40
3	40	1.0	0.80	30	2.5	−0.67
4	10	1.5	−0.90	30	2.5	−0.80
5	10	1.5	0.77	30	2.5	−1.10
6	40	1.5	−0.93	30	2.5	0.70
7	40	1.5	−0.26	30	2.5	−0.70
8	40	1.5	−0.93	30	2.5	−0.20

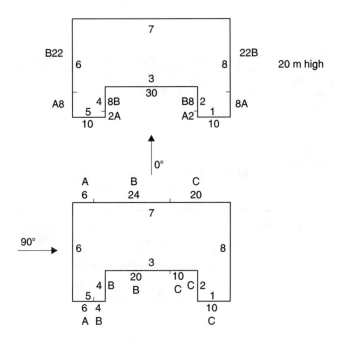

Pressure coefficients for **wide recess** 50 m × 30 m × 20 m high with recess. **Standard method** (Figures 9 and 10, Table 5)

| WD | | 0° | | | 90° | |
Face	b	D/H	C_p	b	D/H	C_p
1	20	1.5	0.77	30	2.5	−0.40
2	20	1.5	−1.00	30	2.5	−0.80
3	40	1.0	0.80	30	2.5	−0.80
4	20	1.5	−1.00	30	2.5	−0.80
5	20	1.5	0.77	30	2.5	−0.95
6	40	1.5	−0.93	30	2.5	0.70
7	40	1.5	−0.26	30	2.5	−0.70
8	40	1.5	−0.93	30	2.5	−0.20

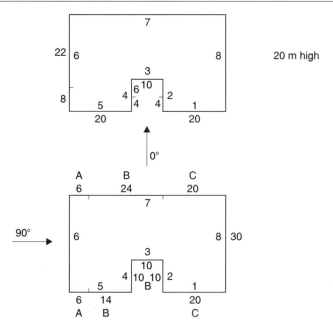

Pressure coefficients for **narrow recess** 50 m × 30 m × 20 m high with recess. **Standard method** (Figures 9 and 10, Table 5)

	WD	0		15		30		45		60		75		90	
Face	D/H	1.5		1.55		1.73		2.12		2.89		2.59		2.50	
	b	40		40		40		40		40		40		30	
		Ar	C_p	Ar	C_p	Ar	C_p	Ar	C_p	Ar	C_p	Ar	C_p	Ar	C_p
1	Theta	0		15		30		45		60		75		90	
	A	160	0.67	160	0.73	160	0.74	160	0.70	160	0.22	160	−1.10	160	−1.30
	B	240	0.79	40	0.83	40	0.74	40	0.62	40	0.42	40	−0.73	–	
	C	–				–				–				–	
	D	–		200	0.65	200	0.46	200	0.30	200	0.22	200	0.14	280	−0.20
	Mean C_p	0.74		0.70		0.60		0.49		0.24		−0.44		−0.53	
2	Theta	0		15		30		45		60		75		90	
	A	160	0.67	160	0.73	160	0.74	160	0.70	160	0.22	160	−1.10	120	−1.30
	B	40	0.79	40	0.83	40	0.74	40	0.62	40	0.42	40	−0.73	80	−1.00
	C	–													
	D	–				–						–		–	
	Mean C_p	0.69		0.75		0.74		0.68		0.26		−1.03		−1.18	
3	Theta	0		15		30		45		60		75		90	
	A	–		–		–						–		–	
	B	200	0.79	200	0.83	200	0.74	200	0.62	200	0.42	200	−0.73	200	−1.00
	C	–		–											
	D	–		–		–		–		–		–		–	
	Mean C_p	0.79		0.83		0.74		0.62		0.42		−0.73		−1.00	
4	Theta	0		15		30		45		60		75		90	
	A	160	0.67	160	0.73	160	0.74	160	0.70	160	0.22	160	−1.10	120	−1.30
	B	40	0.79	40	0.83	40	0.74	40	0.62	40	0.42	40	−0.73	80	−1.00
	C	–				–									
	D	–				–						–		–	
	Mean C_p	0.69		0.75		0.74		0.68		0.26		−1.03		−1.18	
5	Theta	0		15		30		45		60		75		90	
	A	160	0.67	160	0.73	160	0.74	160	0.70	160	0.66	160	−1.10	120	−1.30
	B	40	0.79	240	0.83	240	0.74	240	0.62	240	0.42	240	−0.73	280	−1.00
	C	–		–											
	D	280	0.79	–		–		–		–		–		–	
	Mean C_p	0.74		0.79		0.74		0.65		0.34		−0.88		−1.09	
6	Theta	90		75		60		45		30		15		0	
	A	160	−1.30	160	−1.10	160	0.23	160	0.70	160	0.66	160	0.65	120	−1.30
	B	440	−1.00	440	−0.73	440	0.47	440	0.62	440	0.66	440	0.74	440	0.71
	C	–		–		–		–		–		–		–	
	D	–		–								–		–	
	Mean C_p	−1.08		−0.83		0.41		0.64		0.66		0.72		0.69	
7	Theta	180		165		150		135		120		105		90	
	A	160	−0.31	160	−0.28	160	−0.34	160	−0.50	160	−0.63	160	−0.80	120	−1.30
	B	640	−0.23	640	−0.28	640	−0.34	640	−0.50	640	−0.63	640	−0.73	480	−1.00
	C	–		–											
	D	200	−0.31	200	−0.32	200	−0.32	200	−0.33	200	−0.29	200	−0.26	400	−0.20
	Mean C_p	−0.26		−0.29		−0.34		−0.47		−0.56		−0.65		−0.72	
8	Theta	90		105		120		135		150		165		180	
	A	160	−1.30	160	−0.80	160	−0.63	160	−0.50	160	−0.34	160	−0.25	120	−0.25
	B	440	−1.00	440	−0.73	440	−0.63	440	−0.50	440	−0.34	440	−0.23	480	−0.20
	C	–		–		–									
	D	–		–						–		–		–	
	Mean C_p	−1.08		−0.75		−0.63		−0.50		−0.34		−0.24		−0.21	

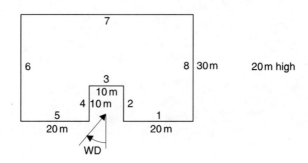

Pressure coefficients for **narrow recess. Directional method**. Sheet 1 (Figure A6, Table A5)

	WD	105		120		135		150		165		180	
Face	D/H	2.59		2.89		2.12		1.73		1.55		1.50	
	b	40		40		40		40		40		40	
		Ar	C_p	Ar	C_p	Ar	C_p	Ar	C_p	Ar	C_p	Ar	C_p
1	Theta	105		120		135		150		165		180	
	A	160	−0.80	160	−0.63	160	−0.50	160	−0.34	160	−0.28	160	−0.31
	B	40	−0.73	40	−0.63	40	−0.50	40	−0.34	40	−0.28	40	−0.23
	C	−				−		−					
	D	200	−0.26	200	−0.29	200	−0.33	200	−0.32	200	−0.32	200	−0.31
	Mean C_p	−0.52		−0.46		−0.42		−0.33		−0.30		−0.30	
2	Theta	105		120		135		150		165		180	
	A	160	−0.80	160	−0.63	160	−0.50	160	−0.34	160	−0.28	160	−0.31
	B	40	−0.73	40	−0.63	40	−0.50	40	−0.34	40	−0.28	40	−0.23
	C	−		−				−		−			
	D	−		−		−		−		−			
	Mean C_p	−0.79		−0.63		−0.50		−0.34		−0.28		−0.29	
3	Theta	105		120		135		150		165		180	
	A	−		−		−							
	B	200	−0.73	200	−0.63	200	−0.50	200	−0.34	200	−0.28	200	−0.23
	C	−		−		−							
	D	−						−					
	Mean C_p	−0.73		−0.63		−0.50		−0.34		−0.28		−0.23	
4	Theta	105		120		135		150		165		180	
	A	160	−0.80	160	−0.63	160	−0.50	160	−0.34	160	−0.28	160	−0.31
	B	40	−0.73	40	−0.63	40	−0.50	40	−0.34	40	−0.28	40	−0.23
	C	−		−		−				−			
	D	−		−		−		−		−		−	
	Mean C_p	−0.79		−0.63		−0.50		−0.34		−0.28		−0.26	
5	Theta	105		120		135		150		165		180	
	A	160	−0.80	160	−0.63	160	−0.50	160	−0.34	160	−0.28	160	−0.31
	B	240	−0.73	40	−0.63	240	−0.50	240	−0.34	240	−0.28	240	−0.23
	C	−		−		−				−		−	
	D	−		−		−		−		−		−	
	Mean C_p	−0.76		−0.63		−0.50		−0.34		−0.28		−0.26	
6	Theta	15		30		45		60		75		90	
	A	160	0.65	160	0.66	160	0.70	160	0.23	160	−1.10	160	−1.30
	B	440	0.74	440	0.66	440	0.62	440	−0.47	440	−0.73	440	−1.00
	C	−								−			
	D	−											
	Mean C_p	0.72		0.66		0.64		0.41		−0.83		−1.08	
7	Theta	75		60		45		30		15		0	
	A	160	−1.10	160	0.21	160	0.70	160	0.74	160	0.73	160	0.67
	B	640	−0.73	640	0.42	640	0.62	640	0.74	640	0.83	640	0.79
	C	−		−		−							
	D	200	0.14	200	0.22	200	0.30	200	0.46	200	0.64	200	0.79
	Mean C_p	−0.62		0.34		0.57		0.69		0.78		0.77	
8	Theta	165		150		135		120		105		90	
	A	160	−0.25	160	−0.34	160	−0.50	160	−0.63	160	−0.80	160	−1.30
	B	440	−0.23	440	−0.34	440	−0.50	440	−0.63	440	−0.73	440	−1.00
	C	−		−		−		−		−		−	
	D	−		−		−		−		−		−	
	Mean C_p	−0.24		−0.34		−0.50		−0.63		−0.75		−1.08	

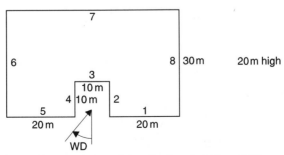

Pressure coefficients for **narrow recess. Directional method** Sheet 2 (Figure A6, Table A5)

Face		0		15		30		45		60		75		90	
	WD	0		15		30		45		60		75		90	
	D/H	1.50		1.55		1.73		2.12		2.89		2.59		2.50	
	b	10/40		17.6/40		23.4/40		40		40		40		30	
		Ar	C_p	Ar	C_p	Ar	C_p	Ar	C_p	Ar	C_p	Ar	C_P	Ar	C_P
1	Theta	0		15		30		45		60		75		90	
	A	40	0.67	160	0.73	160	0.74	160	0.70	160	0.22	160	−1.10	120	−1.30
	B	160	0.79	–		–		–		–		–		80	−1.00
	C	–		–		–		–		–		–		–	
	D	–		40	0.65	40	0.46	40	0.30	40	0.22	40	0.14	–	
	Mean C_p	0.77		0.71		0.68		0.62		0.22		−0.85		−1.18	
2	Theta	90		75		60		45		30		15		0	
	A	–		–		–		–		–		–		–	
	B	–		–		–		–		–		–		–	
	C	200	0.82	200	0.82	200	0.82	200	0.82	200	0.82	200	0.82	200	0.82
	D	–		–		–		–		–		–		–	
	Mean C_p	0.82		0.82		0.82		0.82		0.82		0.82		0.82	
3	Theta	0		15		30		45		60		75		90	
	A	–		–		–		–		–		–		–	
	B	–		–		–		–		–		–		–	
	C	600	0.82	600	0.82	336	0.82	200	0.82	112	0.82	52	0.82	–	
						264	0.66	400	0.48	488	0.33	548	0.23		
	D	–		–		–		–		–		–		600	−0.20
	Mean C_p	0.82		0.82		0.75		0.59		0.42		0.28		−0.20	
														−0.20	
4	Theta	90		105		120		135		150		165		180	
	A	–		40	−1.30	94	−0.63	160	−0.50	160	−0.34	160	−0.25	120	−0.25
	B	–		132	−1.00	106	−0.63	40	−0.50	40	−0.34	40	−0.23	80	−1.00
	C	600	0.82	28	0.82	–		–		–		–		–	
	D	–		–		–		–		–		–		–	
	Mean C_p	0.82		−0.81		−0.63		−0.50		−0.34		−0.24		−0.23	
5	Theta	0		15		30		45		60		75		90	
	A	40	0.67	160	0.73	94	0.74	160	0.70	160	0.22	160	−1.10	120	−1.30
	B	160	0.79	40	0.83	106	0.74	40	0.62	40	0.42	40	−0.73	80	−1.00
	C	–		–		–		–		–		–		–	
	D	–		–		–		–		–		–		–	
	Mean C_D	0.77		0.75		0.74		0.69		0.26		−1.03		−1.18	
6	Theta	90		75		60		45		30		15		0	
	A	40	−1.30	70	−1.10	94	0.23	160	0.70	160	0.22	160	−1.10	120	−1.30
	B	200	−1.00	282	−0.73	374	0.47	440	0.62	440	0.66	440	0.74	480	0.71
	C	200	−0.42	–		–		–		–		–		–	
	D	200	−0.20	248	0.10	132	0.25	–		–		–		–	
	Mean C_p	−0.56		−0.43		0.38		0.64		0.66		0.72		0.69	
7	Theta	180		165		150		135		120		105		90	
	A	160	−0.31	160	−0.28	160	−0.34	160	−0.50	160	−0.63	160	−0.80	120	−1.30
	B	640	−0.23	640	−0.28	640	−0.34	640	−0.50	640	−0.63	640	−0.73	480	−1.00
	C	–		–		–		–		–		–		–	
	D	200	−0.31	200	−0.32	200	−0.32	200	−0.33	200	−0.29	200	−0.26	400	−0.20
	Mean C_p	−0.26		−0.29		−0.34		−0.47		−0.56		−0.65		−0.72	
8	Theta	90		105		120		135		150		165		180	
	A	40	−1.30	160	−0.80	1600	−0.63	1600	−0.50	160	−0.34	160	−0.25	120	−0.25
	B	160	−1.00	440	−0.73	440	−0.63	440	−0.50	440	−0.34	440	−0.23	480	−0.20
	C	200	−0.42	–		–		–		–		–		–	
	D	200	−020	–		–		–		–		–		–	
	Mean C_p	−0.56		−0.75		−0.63		−0.50		−0.34		−0.24		−0.21	

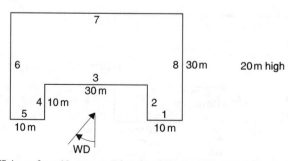

Pressure coefficients for **wide recess. Directional method.** Sheet 1 (Figure A6, Table A5)

	WD	105		120		135		150		165		180	
Face	D/H	2.59		2.89		1.41		1.15		1.55		1.50	
	b	40		40		40		40		40		40	
		Ar	C_p	Ar	C_p	Ar	C_p	Ar	C_p	Ar	C_p	Ar	C_p
1	Theta	105		120		135		150		165		180	
	A	160	−0.80	160	−0.63	160	−0.50	160	−0.34	160	−0.28	160	−0.31
	B	40	−0.73	40	−0.63	40	−0.50	40	−0.34	40	−0.28	40	−0.23
	C	–		–		–		–		–		–	
	D	–		–		–		–		–		–	
	Mean C_p	−0.79		−0.63		−0.50		−0.34		−0.28		−0.29	
2	Theta	15		30		45		60		75		90	
	A	–		–		–		–		–		–	
	B	–		–		–		–		–		–	
	C #	104	−0.48	200	−0.45	200	−0.40	200	−0.26	200	−0.21	200	−0.22
	D	96	0.58	–		–		–		–		–	
	Meacn C_p	0.03		−0.45		−0.40		−0.26		−0.28		−0.22	
3	Theta	105		120		135		150		165		180	
	A	–		–		–		–		–		–	
	B	–		–		–		–		–		–	
	C	600	−0.48	600	−0.45	600	−0.40	600	−0.26	600	−0.21	600	−0.22
	D	–		–		–		–		–		–	
	Mean C_p	−0.48		−0.45		−0.40		−0.26		−0.21		−0.22	
4	Theta	165		150		135		120		105		90	
	A	–		–		–		–		–		–	
	B	–		–		–		–		–		–	
	C	200	−0.19	200	−0.26	200	−0.40	200	−0.45	200	−0.48	200	−0.42
	D	–		–		–		–		–		–	
	Mean C_p	−0.19		−0.26		−0.40		−0.45		−0.48		−0.42	
5	Theta	105		120		135		150		165		180	
	A	160	−0.80	160	−0.63	160	−0.50	160	−0.34	160	−0.28	160	−0.31
	B	40	−0.73	40	−0.63	40	−0.50	40	−0.34	40	−0.28	40	−0.23
	C	–		–		–		–		–		–	
	D	–		–		–		–		–		–	
	Mean C_p	−0.79		−0.63		−0.50		−0.34		−0.28		−0.29	
6	Theta	15		30		45		60		75		90	
	A	160	0.65	160	0.66	160	0.76	160	0.24	160	−1.10	160	−1.30
	B	440	0.74	440	0.66	440	0.66	440	0.50	440	−0.73	440	−1.00
	C	–		–		–		–		–		–	
	D	–		–		–		–		–		–	
	Mean C_p	0.72		0.66		0.69		0.43		−0.83		−1.08	
7	Theta	75		60		45		30		15		0	
	A	160	−1.10	160	0.21	160	0.76	160	0.24	160	−1.10	160	−1.30
	B	640	−0.73	640	0.42	640	0.66	640	0.79	640	0.83	640	0.79
	C	–		–		–		–		–		–	
	D	200	0.14	200	0.22	200	0.33	200	0.48	200	0.64	200	0.79
	Mean C_p	−0.62		0.34		0.61		0.73		0.78		0.77	
8	Theta	165		150		135		120		105		90	
	A	160	−0.25	160	−0.34	160	−0.50	160	−0.63	160	−0.80	160	−1.30
	B	440	−0.23	440	−0.34	440	−0.50	440	−0.63	440	−0.73	440	−1.00
	C	–		–		–		–		–		–	
	D	–		–		–		–		–		–	
	Mean C_p	−0.24		−0.34		−0.50		−0.63		−0.75		−1.08	

As Face 3 Zone C.

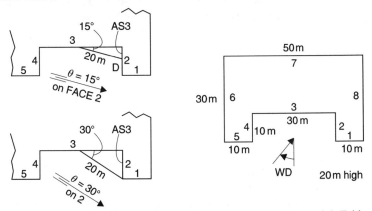

Pressure coefficients for **wide recess. Directional method** Sheet 2 (Figure A6, Table A5)

Group 2. Section 2. Wind load calculations on walls

For a comparison between the wall loads calculated by the Standard and Directional methods, three buildings have been studied. They are rectangular in planform and have wall dimensions 10 m x 20 m, 10 m x 40 m and 50 m x 50 m. They have been studied for two heights 20 m and 100 m.

Each building is presented on two pages; one for the Standard method and the second for the Directional method.

For the Standard-Standard method

Cases 1 and 2 are the orthogonal ones; Cases 3 and 4 are for wind directions 180° and 270°. The larger of Cases 1 and 3, and the larger of Cases 2 and 4 are the two cases for which the stresses must be calculated and 80 per cent of the sum of the stresses considered as another loading case in Section 4.5.3.4 of the Code. If 'any wind direction' is chosen, there will be only two Cases.

TO   is the total load in Newtons * the factor in the rubric (usually 100).
PA   is the panel load in Newtons per square metre (note no factor).
FR   is the load on the front face in Newtons * the factor in the rubric.
RE   is the load on the rear face in Newtons * the factor in the rubric.
SI   is the load on a side face in Newtons * the factor in the rubric.

In the rubric

L   is the length (longer face) in m.
W   is the width in m.
H   is the height in m.
ANW is the angle of the outgoing normal to the longer face east of north. When no preference to direction is stated ANW = 400.

For the Directional-Directional method

The columns represent wind directions in degrees east of north.

PANEL	are panel loads in Newtons per m2 (Pascals). Note there is no factor.
1, 2, 3, 4, etc.	are the faces.
XF	is the overall force in the x-direction (along the longer face of the circumscribing rectangle) in Newtons * the factor in the rubric.
YF	is the overall force in the y-direction (along the shorter face of the circumscribing rectangle) in Newtons * the factor in the rubric.

In the rubric

l	is the longer side of the circumscribing rectangle in m.
w	is the shorter side of the circumscribing rectangle in m.
H	is the height in m.
FACT	is the factor by which the values in the tables must be multiplied to obtain loads in Newtons.
EON	is the angle of the outgoing normal east of north.
a2	is the length of diagonal 'a' used to calculate the wind speed for the internal volume.
a3	is the length of the diagonal 'a' used to calculate the wind speed for the overall load.

	Case number			
	1	2	3	4
TO	5723	1318	5723	1318
PA	−1284	−1284	−1284	−1284
FR	6540	1587	6540	1587
RE	−2932	−648	−2932	−648
SI	−2199	−4309	−2199	−4309
SI	−2199	−4309	−2199	−4309

Standard method loads in Newtons*100

L = 40.0   W = 10.0   H1 = 20.0   ANW = 400.0
H2 = 20.0   H3 = 20.0   H4 = 20.0
Gap = 999.0, 999.0, 999.0, 999.0

	Case number			
	1	2	3	4
TO	3803	614	5427	1276
PA	−879	−856	−921	−931
FR	4309	743	6204	1556
RE	−1923	−304	−2781	−640
SI	−1472	−2184	−2084	−4531
SI	−1472	−2184	−2084	−4531

Standard method loads in Newtons*100

L = 40.0   W = 10.0   H1 = 20.0   ANW = 0.0
H2 = 20.0   H3 = 20.0   H4 = 20.0
Gap = 999.0, 999.0, 999.0, 999.0

	Case number			
	1	2	3	4
TO	3482	1276	5809	670
PA	−805	−864	−864	−795
FR	3945	1556	6641	811
RE	−1761	−640	−2977	−332
SI	−1348	−4531	−2231	−2386
SI	−1348	−4531	−2231	−2386

Standard method loads in Newtons*100

L = 40.0   W = 10.0   H1 = 20.0   ANW = 120.0
H2 = 20.0   H3 = 20.0   H4 = 20.0
Gap = 999.0, 999.0, 999.0, 999.0

	Case number			
	1	2	3	4
TO	5809	1129	2720	964
PA	−1301	−1283	−1225	−1265
FR	6641	1372	3085	1171
RE	−2977	−563	−1378	−480
SI	−2231	−4015	−1052	−3427
SI	−2231	−4015	−1052	−3427

Standard method loads in Newtons*100

L = 40.0   W = 10.0   H1 = 20.0   ANW = 240.0
H2 = 20.0   H3 = 20.0   H4 = 20.0
Gap = 999.0, 999.0, 999.0, 999.0

Wind direction

Face	0	30	60	90	120	150	180	210	240	270	300	330
Panel	−643	−287	−283	−554	−300	−381	−888	−578	−670	−1227	−546	−398
1	3026	2441	1458	−1612	−1761	−1622	−1705	−2507	−4126	−3651	2836	3394
2	−1033	333	604	631	640	444	−1436	−1021	−773	−565	−608	−698
3	−1225	−1219	−1661	−1612	1546	3248	4208	5012	3651	−3651	−3228	−1695
4	−1033	−502	−312	−250	−331	−668	−1436	683	1488	1416	1174	463
NF	2678	1827	1069	576	1134	2431	3718	3734	2625	1301	2074	2539
CF	0	−668	−908	0	962	887	−1	−1366	−2229	0	1760	928
XF	2678	1916	1321	0	−1401	−2549	−3718	−3917	−3423	0	2562	2663
YF	0	334	472	576	501	446	1	−683	−1159	−1301	−916	−465

Loads by Directional method
FL1 = 40.0   FL2 = 10.0   H = 20.0   FAC = 100.0   EON = 0.0
A2 = 200.0   A3 = 45.8
Gaps = 1000.0, 1000.0, 1000.0, 1000.0

Wind direction

Face	0	30	60	90	120	150	180	210	240	270	300	330
Panel	−342	−539	−283	−295	−564	−381	−473	−1082	−670	−655	−1025	−398
1	−2010	−1569	1458	2508	2650	3248	2457	−3222	−4127	−2841	−1968	−1695
2	−378	−243	−312	−516	−905	444	1017	1250	1488	774	−1658	−698
3	1765	−1569	−1662	−1252	−1072	−1622	−2795	−3222	3652	5680	4858	3393
4	731	614	604	342	−905	−668	−526	−498	−773	−1157	−1658	463
NF	1293	561	1069	1877	2346	2429	1796	1148	2629	4235	4293	2538
CF	−1098	0	907	685	−1	−889	−1526	1254	2230	1545	−3	−929
XF	−1598	0	1321	1969	2346	2548	2219	−1254	−3246	−4441	−4293	−2662
YF	−571	−561	−472	−344	0	445	793	1147	1160	777	1	−465

Loads by Directional method
FL1 = 40.0   FL2 = 10.0   H = 20.0   FAC = 100.0   EON = 120.0
A2 = 200.0   A3 = 45.8
Gaps = 1000.0, 1000.0, 1000.0, 1000.0

Wind direction

Face	0	30	60	90	120	150	180	210	240	270	300	330
Panel	−342	−287	−532	−295	−300	−716	−473	−578	−1248	−655	−546	−748
1	−2012	−1219	−1012	−1252	−1760	−2088	2458	5013	6209	5678	2835	−2182
2	731	333	−854	−516	−331	−324	−526	−1021	−2087	774	1174	854
3	1765	2442	2500	2508	1545	−2088	−2797	−2507	−2532	−2841	−3227	−2182
4	−378	−502	−854	342	640	817	1017	683	−2087	−1157	−608	−338
NF	1296	1829	2213	1875	1132	747	1798	3737	5435	4229	2072	780
CF	1099	666	−2	−687	−962	815	1525	1363	−5	−1549	−1762	853
XF	−1600	−1917	−2213	−1967	−1399	815	2220	3919	5435	4437	2561	−854
YF	571	335	0	−343	−500	−747	−793	−684	0	776	916	780

Loads by Directional method
FL1 = 40.0   FL2 = 10.0   H = 20.0   FAC = 100.0   EON = 240.0
A2 = 200.0   A3 = 45.8
Gaps = 1000.0, 1000.0, 1000.0, 1000.0

	Case number			
	1	2	3	4
TO	5723	1318	5723	1318
PA	−1417	−1284	−1417	−1284
FR	6540	1587	6540	1587
RE	−2932	−648	−2932	−648
SI	−2408	−4309	−2408	−4309
SI	−2408	−4309	−2408	−4309

Standard method loads in Newtons*100

L = 40.0   W = 10.0   H1 = 20.0   ANW = 400.0
H2 = 20.0   H3 = 20.0   H4 = 20.0
Gap = 15.0, 15.0, 15.0, 15.0

	Case number			
	1	2	3	4
TO	3803	614	5427	1276
PA	−971	−856	−1031	−931
FR	4309	743	6204	1556
RE	−1923	−304	−2781	−640
SI	−1613	−2184	−2282	−4531
SI	−1613	−2184	−2282	−4531

Standard method loads in Newtons*100

L = 40.0   W = 10.0   H1 = 20.0   ANW = 0.0
H2 = 20.0   H3 = 20.0   H4 = 20.0
Gap = 15.0, 15.0, 15.0, 15.0

	Case number			
	1	2	3	4
TO	3482	1276	5809	670
PA	−889	−864	−947	−795
FR	3945	1556	6641	811
RE	−1761	−640	−2977	−332
SI	−1476	−4531	−2443	−2386
SI	−1476	−4531	−2443	−2386

Standard method loads in Newtons*100

L = 40.0   W = 10.0   H1 = 20.0   ANW = 120.0
H2 = 20.0   H3 = 20.0   H4 = 20.0
Gap = 15.0, 15.0, 15.0, 15.0

	Case number			
	1	2	3	4
TO	5809	1129	2720	964
PA	−1435	−1283	−1359	−1265
FR	6641	1372	3085	1171
RE	−2977	−563	−1378	−480
SI	−2443	−4015	−1152	−3427
SI	−2443	−4015	−1152	−3427

Standard method loads in Newtons*100

L = 40.0   W = 10.0   H1 = 20.0   ANW = 240.0
H2 = 20.0   H3 = 20.0   H4 = 20.0
Gap = 15.0, 15.0, 15.0, 15.0

Wind direction

Face	0	30	60	90	120	150	180	210	240	270	300	330
Panel	−702	−295	−298	−554	−316	−392	−969	−594	−705	−1227	−575	−410
1	3026	2441	1483	−1612	−1804	−1622	−1705	−2507	−4226	−3651	2885	3394
2	−1119	338	604	631	640	450	−1555	−1046	−773	−565	−608	−715
3	−1225	−1219	−1702	−1612	1572	3248	4208	5012	3712	−3651	−3308	−1695
4	−1119	−515	−312	−250	−331	−685	−1555	693	1488	1416	1174	471
NF	2678	1827	1069	576	1134	2431	3718	3734	2625	1301	2074	2539
CF	0	−668	−908	0	962	887	−1	−1366	−2229	0	1760	928
XF	2678	1916	1321	0	−1401	−2549	−3718	−3917	−3423	0	2562	2663
YF	0	334	472	576	501	446	1	−683	−1159	−1301	−916	−465

Loads by Directional method

FL1 = 40.0   FL2 = 10.0   H = 20.0   FAC = 100.0   EON = 0.0
A2 = 200.0   A3 = 45.8
Gaps = 15.0, 15.0, 15.0, 15.0

Wind direction

Face	0	30	60	90	120	150	180	210	240	270	300	330
Panel	−360	−539	−298	−303	−615	−392	−498	−1082	−705	−674	−1118	−410
1	−2060	−1569	1483	2508	2650	3248	2498	−3222	−4228	−2841	−1968	−1695
2	−378	−243	−312	−529	−980	450	1017	1250	1488	785	−1795	−715
3	1795	−1569	−1703	−1252	−1072	−1622	−2864	−3222	3713	5680	4858	3393
4	731	614	604	348	−980	−685	−526	−498	−773	−1185	−1795	471
NF	1293	561	1069	1877	2346	2429	1796	1148	2629	4235	4293	2538
CF	−1098	0	907	685	−1	−889	−1526	1254	2230	1545	−3	−929
XF	−1598	0	1321	1969	2346	2548	2219	−1254	−3246	−4441	−4293	−2662
YF	−571	−561	−472	−344	0	445	793	1147	1160	777	1	−465

Loads by Directional method

FL1 = 40.0   FL2 = 10.0   H = 20.0   FAC = 100.0   EON = 120.0
A2 = 200.0   A3 = 45.8
Gaps = 15.0, 15.0, 15.0, 15.0

Wind direction

Face	0	30	60	90	120	150	180	210	240	270	300	330
Panel	−360	−295	−580	−303	−316	−716	−498	−594	−1360	−674	−575	−748
1	−2061	−1219	−1012	−1252	−1803	−2088	2499	5013	6209	5678	2884	−2182
2	731	338	−924	−529	−331	−324	−526	−1046	−2258	786	1174	854
3	1795	2442	2500	2508	1571	−2088	−2866	−2507	−2532	−2841	−3306	−2182
4	−378	−515	−924	348	640	817	1017	693	−2258	−1185	−608	−338
NF	1296	1829	2213	1875	1132	747	1798	3737	5435	4229	2072	780
CF	1099	666	−2	−687	−962	815	1525	1363	−5	−1549	−1762	853
XF	−1600	−1917	−2213	−1967	−1399	815	2220	3919	5435	4437	2561	−854
YF	571	335	0	−343	−500	−747	−793	−684	0	776	916	780

Loads by Directional method

FL1 = 40.0   FL2 = 10.0   H = 20.0   FAC = 100.0   EON = 240.0
A2 = 200.0   A3 = 45.8
Gaps = 15.0, 15.0, 15.0, 15.0

Case number

	1	2	3	4
TO	5777	5777	5777	5777
PA	−1280	−1280	−1280	−1280
FR	7276	7276	7276	7276
RE	−2836	−2846	−2836	−2836
SI	−7368	−7368	−7368	−7368
SI	−7368	−7368	−7368	−7368

Standard method loads in Newtons*100

L = 50.0   W = 50.0   H1 = 20.0   ANW = 400.0
H2 = 20.0   H3 = 20.0   H4 = 20.0
Gap = 999.0, 999.0, 999.0, 999.0

Case number

	1	2	3	4
TO	3824	2813	5479	5865
PA	−876	−854	−917	−926
FR	4763	3509	6905	7390
RE	−1842	−1359	−2693	−2882
SI	−4841	−3565	−6990	−7482
SI	−4841	−3565	−6990	−7482

Standard method loads in Newtons*100

L = 50.0   W = 50.0   H1 = 20.0   ANW = 0.0
H2 = 20.0   H3 = 20.0   H4 = 20.0
Gap = 999.0, 999.0, 999.0, 999.0

Case number

	1	2	3	4
TO	3501	5865	5865	3072
PA	−802	−859	−859	−792
FR	4361	7390	7390	3832
RE	−1686	−2882	−2882	−1483
SI	−4433	−7482	−7482	−3893
SI	−4433	−7482	−7482	−3893

Standard method loads in Newtons*100

L = 50.0   W = 50.0   H1 = 20.0   ANW = 120.0
H2 = 20.0   H3 = 20.0   H4 = 20.0
Gap = 999.0, 999.0, 999.0, 999.0

Case number

	1	2	3	4
TO	5865	5182	2737	4423
PA	−1297	−1278	−1222	−1261
FR	7390	6496	3413	5544
RE	−2882	−2524	−1321	−2154
SI	−7482	−6588	−3468	−5624
SI	−7482	−6588	−3468	−5624

Standard method loads in Newtons*100

L = 50.0   W = 50.0   H1 = 20.0   ANW = 240.0
H2 = 20.0   H3 = 20.0   H4 = 20.0
Gap = 999.0, 999.0, 999.0, 999.0

Wind direction

Face	0	30	60	90	120	150	180	210	240	270	300	330
Panel	−639	−284	−279	−551	−296	−377	−883	−572	−664	−1220	−540	−394
1	3202	2475	1657	−3149	−2387	−1929	−1773	−2990	−5661	−7136	3231	3443
2	−3653	1681	2439	2760	2585	2239	−5093	−4702	−3612	−2498	−2782	−3178
3	−1269	−1448	−2252	−3149	1756	3296	4467	5104	4215	−7136	−4385	−2015
4	−3653	−2285	−1427	−1094	−1531	−3042	−5093	3479	6159	6273	4752	2339
NF	2559	1978	1948	2205	2065	2630	3563	4070	4870	5008	2786	2747
CF	0	121	−120	0	126	−161	−1	250	−299	−3	230	−168
XF	2559	1652	1078	0	−1142	−2197	−3563	−3400	−2694	−3	2093	2295
YF	0	1094	1627	2205	1725	1455	1	−2252	−4068	−5008	−3163	−1519

Loads by Directional method

FL1 = 50.0   FL2 = 50.0   H = 20.0   FAC = 100.0   EON = 0.0

A2 = 368.0   A3 = 73.5

Gaps = 1000.0, 1000.0, 1000.0, 1000.0

Wind direction

Face	0	30	60	90	120	150	180	210	240	270	300	330
Panel	−338	−536	−279	−291	−560	−377	−468	−1076	−664	−648	−1019	−394
1	−2724	−3065	1656	2543	2805	3295	2799	−6297	−5661	−3388	−2046	−2015
2	−1727	−1064	−1427	−2348	−3201	2239	4117	5535	6158	3943	−5879	−3178
3	2004	−3065	−2252	−1488	−1112	−1929	−3799	−6297	4214	5784	5156	3443
4	2951	2686	2439	1728	−3201	−3042	−2410	−2204	−3612	−5329	−5879	2339
NF	2357	2147	1947	2030	2243	2630	3283	4419	4869	4612	4113	2749
CF	−145	−2	118	−124	498	161	−202	981	298	−284	914	168
XF	−1303	−1	1076	1696	2242	2197	1816	−983	−2694	−3853	−4113	−2296
YF	−1969	−2147	−1626	−1122	499	1455	2742	4418	4067	2551	−915	−1521

Loads by Directional method

FL1 = 50.0   FL2 = 50.0   H = 20.0   FAC = 100.0   EON = 120.0

A2 = 368.0   A3 = 73.5

Gaps = 1000.0, 1000.0, 1000.0, 1000.0

Wind direction

Face	0	30	60	90	120	150	180	210	240	270	300	330
Panel	−338	−284	−528	−291	−296	−712	−468	−572	−1242	−648	−540	−744
1	−2724	−1448	−1049	−1488	−2387	−4079	2799	5104	6674	5783	3231	−4262
2	2950	1681	−3020	−2348	−1513	−1418	−2410	−4702	−7569	3942	4753	3736
3	2004	2476	2646	2543	1756	−4079	−3799	−2990	−2672	−3388	−4385	−4262
4	−1727	−2285	−3020	1727	2586	3576	4117	3479	−7569	−5329	−2782	−1481
NF	2356	1978	2115	2031	2066	2856	3280	4068	5287	4612	3790	2984
CF	144	−122	469	124	−127	631	199	−249	1173	281	−234	662
XF	−1304	−1652	−2114	−1696	−1142	663	1814	3400	5286	3851	2095	−664
YF	1967	1093	−471	−1125	−1726	−2855	−2739	−2247	1177	2553	3166	2983

Loads by Directional method

FL1 = 50.0   FL2 = 50.0   H = 20.0   FAC = 100.0   EON = 240.0

A2 = 368.0   A3 = 73.5

Gaps = 1000.0, 1000.0, 1000.0, 1000.0

Case number

	1	2	3	4
TO	5777	5777	5777	5777
PA	−1478	−1478	−1478	−1478
FR	7276	7276	7276	7276
RE	−2836	−2836	−2836	−2836
SI	−8569	−8569	−8569	−8569
SI	−8569	−8569	−8569	−8569

Standard method loads in Newtons*100

L = 50.0   W = 50.0   H1 = 20.0   ANW = 400.0
H2 = 20.0   H3 = 20.0   H4 = 20.0
Gap = 25.0, 25.0, 25.0, 25.0

Case number

	1	2	3	4
TO	3824	2813	5479	5865
PA	−1013	−991	−1054	−1063
FR	4763	3509	6905	7390
RE	−1842	−1359	−2693	−2882
SI	−5636	−4150	−8129	−8701
SI	−5636	−4150	−8129	−8701

Standard method loads in Newtons*100

L = 50.0   W = 50.0   H1 = 20.0   ANW = 0.0
H2 = 20.0   H3 = 20.0   H4 = 20.0
Gap = 25.0, 25.0, 25.0, 25.0

Case number

	1	2	3	4
TO	3501	5865	5865	3072
PA	−927	−985	−985	−918
FR	4361	7390	7390	3832
RE	−1686	−2882	−2882	−1483
SI	−5161	−8701	−8701	−4532
SI	−5161	−8701	−8701	−4532

Standard method loads in Newtons*100

L = 50.0   W = 50.0   H1 = 20.0   ANW = 120.0
H2 = 20.0   H3 = 20.0   H4 = 20.0
Gap = 25.0, 25.0, 25.0, 25.0

Case number

	1	2	3	4
TO	5865	5182	2737	4423
PA	−1498	−1480	−1423	−1462
FR	7390	6496	3413	5544
RE	−2882	−2524	−1321	−2154
SI	−8701	−7666	−4037	−6543
SI	−8701	−7666	−4037	−6543

Standard method loads in Newtons*100

L = 50.0   W = 50.0   H1 = 20.0   ANW = 240.0
H2 = 20.0   H3 = 20.0   H4 = 20.0
Gap = 25.0, 25.0, 25.0, 25.0

Wind direction

Face	0	30	60	90	120	150	180	210	240	270	300	330
Panel	−756	−291	−287	−651	−304	−387	−1044	−587	−681	−1441	−554	−404
1	3202	2475	1674	−3492	−2424	−1929	−1773	−2990	−5748	−7911	3265	3443
2	−4051	1699	2439	2760	2585	2263	−5648	−4776	−3612	−2498	−2782	−3228
3	−1269	−1448	−2287	−3492	1774	3296	4467	5104	4258	−7911	−4454	−2015
4	−4051	−2321	−1427	−1094	−1531	−3089	−5648	3515	6159	6273	4752	2364
NF	2559	1978	1948	2205	2065	2630	3563	4070	4870	5008	3786	2747
CF	0	121	−120	0		−161	−1	250	−299	−3	230	−168
XF	2559	1652	1078	0	−1142	−2197	−3563	−3400	−2694	−3	2093	2295
YF	0	1094	1627	2205	1725	1455	1	−2252	−4068	−5008	−3163	−1519

Loads by Directional method

FL1 = 50.0   FL2 = 50.0   H = 20.0   FAC = 100.0   EON = 0.0
A2 = 368.0   A3 = 73.5
Gaps = 25.0, 25.0, 25.0, 25.0

Wind direction

Face	0	30	60	90	120	150	180	210	240	270	300	330
Panel	−347	−634	−287	−299	−662	−387	−480	−1271	−681	−665	−1205	−404
1	−2767	−3399	1674	2543	2805	3295	2829	−6981	−5748	−3388	−2046	−2015
2	−1727	−1064	−1427	−2385	−3550	2263	4117	5535	6158	3984	−6519	−3228
3	2025	−3399	−2287	−1488	−1112	−1929	−3858	−6981	4258	5784	5156	3443
4	2951	2686	2439	1746	−3550	−3089	−2410	−2204	−3612	−5412	−6519	2364
NF	2357	2147	1947	2030	2243	2630	3283	4419	4869	4612	4113	2749
CF	−145	−2	118	−124	498	161	−202	981	298	−284	914	168
XF	−1303	−1	1076	1696	2242	2197	1816	−983	−2694	−3853	−4113	−2296
YF	−1969	−2147	−1626	−1122	499	1455	2742	4418	4067	2551	−915	−1521

Loads by Directional method

FL1 = 50.0   FL2 = 50.0   H = 20.0   FAC = 100.0   EON = 120.0
A2 = 368.0   A3 = 73.5
Gaps = 25.0, 25.0, 25.0, 25.0

Wind direction

Face	0	30	60	90	120	150	180	210	240	270	300	330
Panel	−347	−291	−625	−299	−304	−842	−480	−587	−1466	−665	−554	−879
1	−2766	−1448	−1049	−1488	−2424	−4523	2828	5104	6674	5783	3265	−4726
2	2950	1699	−3349	−2385	−1513	−1418	−2410	−4776	−8387	3983	4753	3736
3	2025	2476	2646	2543	1775	−4523	−3858	−2990	−2672	−3388	−4454	−4726
4	−1727	−2321	−3349	1745	2586	3576	4117	3516	−8387	−5412	−2782	−1481
NF	2356	1978	2115	2031	2066	2856	3280	4068	5287	4612	3790	2984
CF	144	−122	469	124	−127	631	199	−249	1173	281	−234	662
XF	−1304	−1652	−2114	−1696	−1142	663	1814	3400	5286	3851	2095	−664
YF	1967	1093	−471	−1125	−1726	−2855	−2739	−2247	1177	2553	3166	2983

Loads by Directional method

FL1 = 50.0   FL2 = 50.0   H = 20.0   FAC = 100.0   EON = 240.0
A2 = 368.0   A3 = 73.5
Gaps = 25.0, 25.0, 25.0, 25.0

Group 2 Section 3. Wind load calculations on walls, non-rectangular buildings

The data for three series of buildings are presented in this section. At the top of every page the data for the building of the circumscribing rectangle are presented, followed down the page by three different buildings with the same circumscribing rectangle. This allows the effect of shape to be understood.

Data are presented in the first series for three different directions of north relative to the major face of the rectangle. In the second and third series only two directions of north relative to the main face are studied. In every case the loads are determined for all wind directions.

Refer to top example on p. 113

Wind direction

Face	0	30	60	90	120	150	180	210	240	270	300	330
Panel	−284	−343	−222	−424	−249	−584	−209	−789	−507	−870	−430	−477
1	2865	2248	1404	−1538	−1290	−1237	−1481	−1915	−3014	−3484	2761	3144
2	−326	−480	256	466	430	556	343	−1093	−743	−468	−359	−281
3	−849	−812	−1071	−1036	1538	2475	3145	3547	1175	−2894	−2141	−1041
4	−575	−313	−276	−326	−504	−1070	637	1370	1512	1478	786	−954
NF	2671	1687	816	422	1151	2331	3350	3318	2448	1172	1684	2372
CF	−2	−976	−943	815	964	799	−109	−1109	−2064	−690	1606	1366
XF	2671	1949	1225	−815	−1410	−2418	−3350	−3428	−3012	−690	2233	2738
YF	−2	−1	235	422	515	473	109	−698	−1088	−1172	−655	−2

Loads by Directional method

FL1 = 40.0   FL2 = 8.0   H = 20.0   FAC = 100.0   EON = 0.0

A2 = 200.0   A3 = 45.8

Gaps = 1000.0, 1000.0, 1000.0, 1000.0

Wind direction

Face	0	30	60	90	120	150	180	210	240	270	300	330
Panel	−330	−363	−227	−392	−201	−258	−462	−967	−559	−1135	−508	−249
1	2683	2117	1327	−1451	−1220	−1116	−1392	−1799	−2858	−3285	−2637	−3053
2	−467	−686	405	657	691	891	640	−1620	−1171	−737	−544	−435
3	−1037	−850	−1200	−1447	585	2617	3586	4383	3886	−2583	−2639	−1468
4	−416	−429	−272	−178	−182	−313	−555	−1141	880	975	746	556
NF	2589	1587	833	518	1098	2378	3484	3293	2276	956	1917	2547
CF	−223	−917	−765	301	999	876	−260	−1152	−2039	−1253	2006	1006
XF	2589	1833	1079	−301	−1414	−2497	−3484	−3428	−2904	−1253	−2696	−2709
YF	−223	0	339	518	451	430	260	−648	−951	−956	−656	−402

Loads by Directional method

FL1 = 37.5   FL2 = 11.5   H = 20.0   FAC = 100.0   EON = 0.0

A2 = 200.0   A3 = 45.8

Gaps = 1000.0, 1000.0, 1000.0, 1000.0

Wind direction

Face	0	30	60	90	120	150	180	210	240	270	300	330
Panel	−160	−137	−168	−403	−426	−257	−231	−283	−507	−894	−386	−344
1	2349	1963	1238	−1303	−1097	−1072	−1324	−1604	−2801	−2945	2163	2654
2	656	580	544	541	−477	−480	−440	−413	−482	−623	−691	−635
3	−465	−444	−594	−660	995	1542	2004	2320	−916	−1920	−1313	−645
4	−633	−539	−567	−759	−1201	1420	2217	2375	2797	1518	−1059	−542
NF	2560	1977	1071	390	602	1827	3531	4101	2695	779	1100	1987
CF	393	−699	−1081	83	798	1412	627	−1323	−2725	−1556	1915	1442
XF	2560	2047	1417	−83	−992	−2288	−3531	−4213	−3708	−1556	2208	2442
YF	393	408	386	390	122	−309	−627	−904	−971	−779	4	255

Loads by Directional method

FL1 = 32.5   FL2 = 10.5   H = 20.0   FAC = 100.0   EON = 0.0

A2 = 200.0   A3 = 45.8

Gaps = 1000.0, 1000.0, 1000.0, 1000.0

Refer to middle example on p. 113

Wind direction

Face	0	30	60	90	120	150	180	210	240	270	300	330
Panel	−229	−343	−202	−452	−249	−456	−371	−829	−559	−1000	−242	−545
1	−1462	−1497	1420	2324	2509	2991	2365	−3075	−3035	−2170	−1710	−1292
2	−326	−184	−169	−189	−286	−638	431	923	1002	964	395	−749
3	563	−1234	−1015	−714	−744	−1081	−1802	−2068	3608	4314	3631	2407
4	788	658	418	−827	−504	−417	−466	−649	−1171	−1850	736	935
NF	1206	505	868	1754	2339	2242	1371	841	2669	4062	3867	2255
CF	−1017	−298	828	1009	−2	−1298	−1585	1623	2233	1390	−127	−755
XF	−1484	−297	1151	2024	2339	2591	2058	−1623	−3269	−4213	−3867	−2330
YF	−536	−506	−337	−1	−2	−2	395	840	1193	824	125	`−474

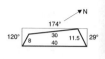

Loads by Directional method

FL1 = 40.0   FL2 = 8.0   H = 20.0   FAC = 100.0   EON = 120.0
A2 = 200.0   A3 = 45.8
Gaps = 1000.0, 1000.0, 1000.0, 1000.0

Wind direction

Face	0	30	60	90	120	150	180	210	240	270	300	330
Panel	−229	−462	−245	−173	−289	−483	−379	−768	−453	−445	−533	−668
1	−1388	−1412	1356	2257	2349	2816	2237	−2899	−2870	−1957	−1607	−1214
2	−467	−276	−245	−272	−409	−913	683	1303	1607	1545	738	−1110
3	1847	−1099	−1285	−1024	−908	−1131	−2021	−2887	1415	4570	4139	2973
4	432	423	386	415	−364	−571	−459	−355	−427	−543	−641	−783
NF	1121	412	988	1883	2267	2110	1400	1031	2545	4143	4022	2238
CF	−1005	−540	1034	743	−196	−1220	−1285	599	2314	1524	−301	−784
XF	−1430	−540	1390	2002	2267	2437	1813	−600	−3277	−4351	−4022	−2330
YF	−468	−412	−338	−297	−195	0	570	1031	1045	749	300	−440

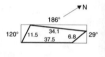

Loads by Directional method

FL1 = 37.5   FL2 = 11.5   H = 20.0   FAC = 100.0   EON = 120.0
A2 = 200.0   A3 = 45.8
Gaps = 1000.0, 1000.0, 1000.0, 1000.0

Wind direction

Face	0	30	60	90	120	150	180	210	240	270	300	330
Panel	−257	−392	−364	−349	−140	−182	−282	−789	−946	−444	−267	−194
1	−1364	−1268	1112	1962	2057	2612	2085	−2600	−2576	−1877	−1529	−1109
2	−283	−339	−473	−626	574	773	917	1075	−1108	−834	−508	−279
3	−406	−683	−546	−391	−407	−591	−1000	−1314	2329	2682	2313	1580
4	1517	650	−1088	−832	−554	−717	−955	−1512	−2793	2474	2560	1615
NF	1327	336	568	1469	2243	2629	1798	776	1395	3184	4077	2788
CF	−1343	−671	987	1066	344	−891	−1816	165	1850	2460	723	−901
XF	−1826	−671	1139	1805	2243	2722	2472	−166	−2300	−3987	−4077	−2864
YF	−478	−336	2	189	345	543	650	776	282	−540	−724	−614

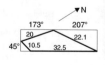

Loads by Directional method

FL1 = 32.5   FL2 = 10.5   H = 20.0   FAC = 100.0   EON = 120.0
A2 = 200.0   A3 = 45.8
Gaps = 1000.0, 1000.0, 1000.0, 1000.0

Refer to bottom example on p. 113

Wind direction

Face	0	30	60	90	120	150	180	210	240	270	300	330
Panel	−284	−439	−125	−353	−201	−456	−338	−883	−559	−783	−429	−572
1	−1473	−929	−879	−955	−1280	−1992	2392	4646	5883	5232	2730	−2082
2	465	383	191	−493	−286	−245	−285	−378	−666	−1103	498	630
3	1757	1860	1835	1746	493	−1642	−1709	−1429	−1755	−1889	−2080	−1403
4	−575	−805	378	691	690	876	705	−1633	−1171	−725	−538	−442
NF	1316	1754	1993	1666	1055	673	1460	3492	5420	3904	1581	572
CF	1100	600	−66	−558	−891	419	1392	2008	−9	−2263	−1829	1104
XF	−1611	−1819	−1993	−1772	−1299	420	1936	4028	5420	4512	2375	−1140
YF	588	355	64	−351	−469	−672	−567	−3	−4	−4	456	571

Loads by Directional method
FL1 = 40.0   FL2 = 8.0   H = 20.0   FAC = 100.0   EON = 240.0
A2 = 200.0   A3 = 45.8
Gaps = 1000.0, 1000.0, 1000.0, 1000.0

Wind direction

Face	0	30	60	90	120	150	180	210	240	270	300	330
Panel	−229	−194	−276	−495	−201	−614	−411	−342	−646	−828	−438	−530
1	−1394	−838	−826	−897	−1215	−1879	2284	4508	5504	4922	2582	−1964
2	739	596	356	−705	−409	−367	−413	−542	−955	−1580	789	889
3	667	1967	2130	2175	1641	−1462	−2164	−2048	−2142	−1981	−2333	−1958
4	−208	−235	−330	−578	378	563	651	822	−844	−987	−530	−241
NF	1254	1789	2073	1653	981	548	1662	3748	5253	3674	1615	701
CF	1140	657	−156	−580	−880	−718	1738	1477	−457	−2126	−1484	407
XF	−1615	−1878	−2073	−1722	−1252	−718	2337	3985	5253	4245	2092	−408
YF	515	323	154	−325	−410	−549	−568	−591	−452	0	658	701

Loads by Directional method
FL1 = 37.5   FL2 = 11.5   H = 20.0   FAC = 100.0   EON = 240.0
A2 = 200.0   A3 = 45.8
Gaps = 1000.0, 1000.0, 1000.0, 1000.0

Wind direction

Face	0	30	60	90	120	150	180	210	240	270	300	330
Panel	−486	−261	−179	−143	−225	−521	−609	−683	−321	−315	−326	−545
1	−1253	−806	−786	−819	−1195	−1688	1874	3914	4812	4558	2406	−1764
2	−718	−480	−334	−252	−248	−451	−796	−1239	1339	1340	1059	733
3	1137	1159	1110	1078	−355	−908	−920	−782	−963	−1032	−1155	−894
4	−1372	1067	1317	1369	1328	865	−1831	−1656	−1306	−1253	−1102	−1028
NF	688	1375	2102	2060	1162	446	955	2926	5197	4578	2075	528
CF	912	1062	372	−666	−1176	−893	1659	2121	795	−1554	−2097	113
XF	−1134	−1722	−2101	−2117	−1599	−892	1914	3594	5196	4741	2853	−113
YF	138	−233	−373	−454	−419	−447	3	376	799	946	750	527

Loads by Directional method
FL1 = 32.5   FL2 = 10.5   H = 20.0   FAC = 100.0   EON = 240.0
A2 = 200.0   A3 = 45.8
Gaps = 1000.0, 1000.0, 1000.0, 1000.0

Refer to examples on pp. 125, 126 and 127

Wind direction

Face	0	30	60	90	120	150	180	210	240	270	300	330
Panel	−642	−286	−282	−553	−299	−380	−887	−576	−668	−1224	−544	−397
1	2301	1835	1197	−1571	−1525	−1229	−1287	−1895	−3554	−3542	2329	2550
2	−1661	786	1207	1293	1279	1045	−2308	−2017	−1526	−1165	−1196	−1375
3	−924	−923	−1438	−1571	1269	2440	3199	3756	2987	−3542	−2794	−1284
4	−1661	−990	−615	−515	−652	−1316	−2308	1610	2979	2909	2345	1092
NF	2039	1564	1298	1170	1377	2079	2830	3191	3178	2635	2517	2171
CF	0	−139	−379	0	401	184	−1	−283	−927	−1	733	193
XF	2039	1424	977	0	−1036	−1893	−2830	−2905	−2392	−1	1894	1977
YF	0	661	935	1170	991	880	109	−1349	−2288	−2635	−1813	−918

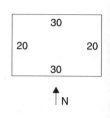

Loads by Directional method
FL1 = 30.0   FL2 = 20.0   H = 20.0   FAC = 100.0   EON = 0.0
A2 = 229.0   A3 = 41.2
Gaps = 1000.0, 1000.0, 1000.0, 1000.0

Wind direction

Face	0	30	60	90	120	150	180	210	240	270	300	330
Panel	−341	−538	−282	−294	−562	−380	−472	−1080	−668	−653	−1023	−397
1	−1741	−1529	1197	1885	2015	2440	2017	−3127	−3554	−2147	−1486	−1284
2	−744	−501	−615	−1017	−1455	1045	2031	2568	2979	1825	−2664	−1375
3	1449	−1529	−1438	−949	−810	−1229	−2421	−3127	2987	4256	3693	2550
4	1460	1258	1206	807	−1455	−1316	−1036	−1028	−1526	−2286	−2664	1092
NF	1572	1140	1298	1606	1785	2079	2182	2324	3178	3616	3265	2172
CF	−458	−1	378	142	−1	−185	−637	−2	926	320	−2	−193
XF	−1183	0	977	1462	1785	1893	1642	1	−2393	−3292	−3265	−1977
YF	−1132	−1140	−934	−678	0	879	1571	2324	2288	1529	1	−919

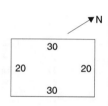

Loads by Directional method
FL1 = 30.0   FL2 = 20.0   H = 20.0   FAC = 100.0   EON = 120.0
A2 = 229.0   A3 = 41.2
Gaps = 1000.0, 1000.0, 1000.0, 1000.0

Wind direction

Face	0	30	60	90	120	150	180	210	240	270	300	330
Panel	−341	−286	−531	−294	−299	−715	−472	−576	−1246	−653	−544	−747
1	−1741	−923	−764	−949	−1525	−2035	2017	3756	4703	4256	2329	−2126
2	1460	786	−1372	−1017	−652	−667	−1036	−2017	−3365	1825	2345	1748
3	1449	1835	1900	1885	1269	−2035	−2421	−1895	−1908	−2147	−2794	−2126
4	−744	−990	−1372	807	1279	1673	2031	1610	−3365	−2286	−1196	−697
NF	1572	1564	1683	1606	1376	1515	2182	3190	4121	3614	2518	1583
CF	458	138	−2	−143	−402	−2	635	282	−3	−323	−736	647
XF	−1184	−1424	−1683	−1462	−1035	−1	1642	2905	4121	3290	1895	−649
YF	1131	661	0	−680	−992	−1515	−1570	−1347	0	1529	1814	1582

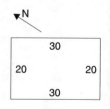

Loads by Directional method
FL1 = 30.0   FL2 = 20.0   H = 20.0   FAC = 100.0   EON = 240.0
A2 = 229.0   A3 = 41.2
Gaps = 1000.0, 1000.0, 1000.0, 1000.0

Refer to examples on pp. 124, 126 and 127

Wind direction

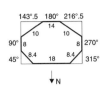

Face	0	30	60	90	120	150	180	210	240	270	300	330
Panel	−467	−339	−405	−402	−354	−345	−645	−524	−789	−892	−781	−470
1	1288	1064	704	−1145	−709	−595	−743	−917	−1651	−2570	1368	1479
2	529	459	464	457	−512	−512	−450	−394	−466	−627	−737	−684
3	−636	245	429	454	455	326	−884	−622	−492	−442	−385	−425
4	−332	−398	−680	527	601	739	921	−412	−1410	−832	−447	−327
5	−417	−349	−523	−903	559	1081	1354	1656	1313	−2024	−1016	−486
6	−332	−235	−229	−370	−610	−267	921	1132	1397	1185	−1321	−554
7	−636	−305	−198	−196	−210	−406	−884	503	1059	1019	834	341
8	529	−492	−379	−279	−198	−256	−450	−783	−1182	1027	901	638
NF	1862	1408	1102	987	1167	1874	2616	2873	2694	2222	2136	1957
CF	0	−294	−269	54	234	432	−1	−663	−541	−124	522	408
XF	1862	1367	784	−54	−786	−1839	−2616	−2820	−1816	−124	1520	1899
YF	0	449	819	987	893	562	0	−861	−2063	−2222	−1589	−624

Loads by Directional method
FL1 = 18.0   FL2 = 8.4   H = 20.0   FAC = 100.0   EON = 0.0
A2 = 229.0   A3 = 41.2
Gaps = 1000.0, 1000.0, 1000.0, 1000.0

Wind direction

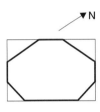

Face	0	30	60	90	120	150	180	210	240	270	300	330
Panel	−404	−391	−405	−348	−409	−450	−677	−787	−789	−593	−745	−360
1	−809	−1115	703	1093	1128	1415	1186	−2268	−1651	−1039	−858	−622
2	−226	−271	−379	−506	463	610	781	907	−1182	−887	−520	−267
3	−239	−190	−198	−314	−557	326	723	899	1058	571	−1020	−425
4	−697	−360	−229	−242	−291	−530	−1144	1045	1396	1283	1063	−279
5	638	−879	−523	−359	−365	−465	−880	−1786	1312	1877	1563	1129
6	686	513	−680	−409	−291	−313	−387	−734	−1410	−467	1063	772
7	520	442	429	252	−557	−406	−334	−390	−492	−705	−1020	341
8	−584	445	464	471	463	−655	−639	−554	−466	−447	−520	−535
NF	1333	961	1101	1447	1631	1872	1852	1961	2693	3258	3019	1955
CF	−267	−54	269	301	0	−391	−453	108	540	750	−2	−452
XF	−898	−53	784	1404	1631	1816	1318	−109	−1815	−3198	−3019	−1919
YF	−1020	−961	−819	−461	0	597	1378	1961	2062	977	0	−586

Loads by Directional method
FL1 = 18.0   FL2 = 8.4   H = 20.0   FAC = 100.0   EON = 120.0
A2 = 229.0   A3 = 41.2
Gaps = 1000.0, 1000.0, 1000.0, 1000.0

Wind direction

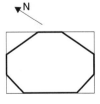

Face	0	30	60	90	120	150	180	210	240	270	300	330
Panel	−404	−260	−386	−267	−354	−520	−677	−682	−910	−772	−781	−543
1	−809	−447	−441	−460	−709	−1483	1185	2171	2627	2459	1369	−1549
2	−584	−385	−267	−198	−210	−254	−639	−1000	1078	1059	902	618
3	519	245	−525	−314	−210	−254	−334	−622	−1284	571	835	614
4	686	556	547	−206	−610	−479	−387	−482	−681	−919	−1321	713
5	638	813	804	835	559	−1169	−880	−716	−858	−811	−1016	−1222
6	−697	−201	547	571	601	682	−1144	−811	−681	−546	−447	−501
7	−239	−305	−525	252	455	587	723	503	−1284	−705	−385	−265
8	−226	−192	−267	−395	−512	592	781	934	1078	−1132	−737	−377
NF	1332	1410	1556	1446	1167	1278	1851	2875	3764	3254	2137	1335
CF	267	324	−1	−334	−234	−72	452	598	−3	−681	−523	73
XF	−898	−1384	−1556	−1419	−786	−71	1318	2790	3764	3158	1520	−74
YF	1020	422	0	−434	−894	−1278	−1376	−917	0	1039	1590	1335

Loads by Directional method
FL1 = 18.0   FL2 = 8.4   H = 20.0   FAC = 100.0   EON = 240.0
A2 = 229.0   A3 = 41.2
Gaps = 1000.0, 1000.0, 1000.0, 1000.0

126 Examples

Refer to examples on pp. 124, 125 and 127

Wind direction

Face	0	30	60	90	120	150	180	210	240	270	300	330
Panel	−228	−427	−526	−458	−351	−707	−472	−1068	−783	−1015	−1014	−592
1	1323	1101	716	−1183	−792	−652	−769	−1004	−1842	−2654	1394	1530
2	−375	885	930	1009	887	−1526	−1257	−1058	−990	−972	−1289	−1339
3	−405	−500	−784	563	667	751	921	−399	−1410	−832	−448	−327
4	−417	−349	−523	−903	562	1089	1354	1670	1320	−2024	−1016	−486
5	−332	−235	−230	−370	−610	−259	921	1152	1546	1265	1523	−695
6	−398	−963	−663	−431	−422	−690	−1257	−2328	2065	2267	1808	1231
NF	1676	1348	1148	1017	1122	1736	2616	2661	2592	2290	2225	1873
CF	0	−19	−250	0	160	361	−1	−553	−369	−3	484	25
XF	1676	1177	790	0	−700	−1684	−2616	−2582	−1616	−3	1531	1635
YF	0	657	869	1017	892	555	0	−851	−2060	−2290	−1684	−914

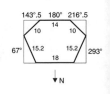

Loads by Directional method
FL1 = 18.0   FL2 = 15.2   H = 20.0   FAC = 100.0   EON = 0.0
A2 = 229.0   A3 = 41.2
Gaps = 1000.0, 1000.0, 1000.0, 1000.0

Wind direction

Face	0	30	60	90	120	150	180	210	240	270	300	330
Panel	−517	−446	−405	−386	−199	−567	−878	−896	−783	−1211	−544	−738
1	−904	−1151	716	1131	1159	1464	1207	−2342	−1842	−1138	−888	−682
2	−456	−383	−594	−941	−328	1178	1566	2001	2065	−2640	−1451	−721
3	−796	−449	−275	−282	−355	−665	−1319	1116	1547	1304	1063	−270
4	642	−879	−523	−359	−365	−465	−880	−1787	1320	1891	1563	1138
5	691	512	−680	−409	−291	−313	−388	−734	−1410	−453	1063	786
6	1012	982	959	970	−349	−1281	−1117	−858	−991	−1199	−1451	−1593
NF	1282	990	1147	1385	1468	1792	1929	2020	2591	3019	3019	1811
CF	−183	−1	249	18	0	−26	−421	1	369	627	−2	−377
XF	−799	−1	790	1209	1468	1565	1328	−1	−1616	−2928	−3019	−1757
YF	−1019	−990	−868	−675	0	874	1460	2020	2058	964	0	−580

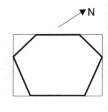

Loads by Directional method
FL1 = 18.0   FL2 = 15.2   H = 20.0   FAC = 100.0   EON = 120.0
A2 = 229.0   A3 = 41.2
Gaps = 1000.0, 1000.0, 1000.0, 1000.0

Wind direction

Face	0	30	60	90	120	150	180	210	240	270	300	330
Panel	−401	−467	−282	−547	−453	−592	−677	−756	−450	−971	−1041	−619
1	−904	−490	−456	−504	−792	−1531	1207	2245	2698	2544	1394	−1600
2	983	−1086	−666	−482	−399	−510	−1001	−1862	−776	2046	1808	1365
3	761	626	629	−230	−697	−597	−464	−561	−826	−1152	−1522	762
4	642	819	804	841	563	−1169	−880	−716	−858	−811	−1016	−1222
5	−697	−195	547	581	606	682	−1145	−811	−681	−546	−448	−501
6	−482	−518	−747	−1178	887	1306	1614	1925	−822	−2218	−1289	−583
NF	1281	1306	1556	1339	1123	1317	1928	2751	3388	3116	2226	1375
CF	182	271	−1	−279	−160	−2	419	36	0	−46	−486	0
XF	−799	−1267	−1556	−1299	−699	−1	1328	2402	3388	2720	1532	−1
YF	1018	417	0	−429	−893	−1317	−1459	−1342	2	1520	1686	1375

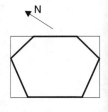

Loads by Directional method
FL1 = 18.0   FL2 = 15.2   H = 20.0   FAC = 100.0   EON = 240.0
A2 = 229.0   A3 = 41.2
Gaps = 1000.0, 1000.0, 1000.0, 1000.0

Refer to examples on pp. 124, 125 and 126

Wind direction

Face	0	30	60	90	120	150	180	210	240	270	300	330
Panel	-318	-499	-321	-402	-449	-520	-366	-787	-998	-892	-620	-693
1	1289	1076	713	-1145	-709	-595	-743	-917	-1651	-2570	1386	1496
2	529	476	524	511	-594	-637	-549	-464	-554	-763	-916	-794
3	-889	-1100	640	1021	991	1265	1035	-2045	-1471	-926	-741	-554
4	-417	-349	-523	-903	566	1097	1355	1681	1329	-2024	-1016	-486
5	-721	-398	-381	-409	-632	-1338	1035	1939	2421	2296	1245	-1529
6	616	-571	-472	-340	-236	-302	-549	-972	-1369	1147	1018	662
NF	1860	1268	1016	1005	1234	1717	2278	2635	2849	2263	1970	1763
CF	0	-535	-176	146	227	-67	0	102	-525	-331	341	744
XF	1860	1366	661	-146	-814	-1453	-2278	-2231	-1879	-331	1280	1898
YF	0	170	792	1005	955	917	0	-1406	-2204	-2263	-1535	-237

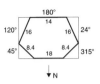

Loads by Directional method
FL1 = 18.0   FL2 = 8.4   H = 20.0   FAC = 100.0   EON = 0.0
A2 = 229.0   A3 = 41.2
Gaps = 1000.0, 1000.0, 1000.0, 1000.0

Wind direction

Face	0	30	60	90	120	150	180	210	240	270	300	330
Panel	-513	-391	-256	-402	-279	-663	-537	-787	-998	-892	-423	-543
1	-809	-1151	713	1106	1129	1431	1201	-2268	-1651	-1039	-858	-622
2	-229	-271	-379	-504	-463	633	882	1012	-1369	-1102	-634	-316
3	-889	-475	-406	-488	-779	-1463	1078	2026	2306	2197	1194	-1398
4	646	-879	-523	-359	-365	-465	-880	-1787	1328	1905	1564	1146
5	1132	952	623	-1033	-632	-530	-642	-817	-1471	-2317	1194	1321
6	-678	497	524	546	539	-760	-794	-674	-554	-526	-634	-666
NF	1409	979	1015	1304	1630	1686	1708	1998	2848	2986	2629	1794
CF	-260	-143	176	549	0	-712	-296	290	524	-119	0	69
XF	-929	-143	660	1404	1630	1816	1110	-291	-1879	-2527	-2629	-1518
YF	-1090	-979	-791	-175	0	226	1331	1998	2204	1595	0	-957

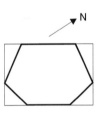

Loads by Directional method
FL1 = 18.0   FL2 = 8.4   H = 20.0   FAC = 100.0   EON = 120.0
A2 = 229.0   A3 = 41.2
Gaps = 1000.0, 1000.0, 1000.0, 1000.0

Wind direction

Face	0	30	60	90	120	150	180	210	240	270	300	330
Panel	-404	-391	-219	-513	-449	-520	-428	-787	-625	-1136	-620	-543
1	-809	-447	-441	-460	-709	-1483	1201	2196	2627	2487	1386	-1549
2	-584	-385	-267	-198	-200	-361	-639	-995	1079	1099	1018	691
3	1188	1008	634	-1130	-779	-631	-685	-971	-1808	-2534	-1245	1381
4	646	825	805	847	566	-1169	-880	-716	-858	-811	-1016	-1222
5	-721	-1006	614	977	991	1266	1051	-2045	-1471	-926	-741	-554
6	-270	-227	-326	-492	-593	662	882	1081	1252	-1313	-916	-460
NF	1409	1292	1355	1326	1234	1301	1707	2591	3761	2930	1971	1360
CF	259	-51	0	50	-228	-191	296	1091	-3	-1239	-342	197
XF	-930	-1093	-1355	-1123	-814	-190	1111	2790	3761	3157	1280	-198
YF	1090	690	0	-708	-955	-1301	-1329	-347	0	393	1536	1360

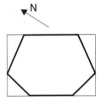

Loads by Directional method
FL1 = 18.0   FL2 = 8.4   H = 20.0   FAC = 100.0   EON = 240.0
A2 = 229.0   A3 = 41.2
Gaps = 1000.0, 1000.0, 1000.0, 1000.0

Group 2. Section 4. Wind load calculations on flat roofs, non-rectangular buildings

The following is the procedure suggested on p. 21 of the Handbook.
The building plan is shown below.

Height = 20 m

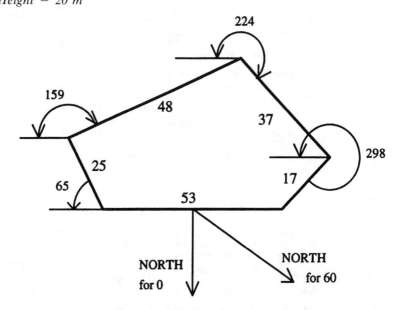

This drawing has been traced 12 times onto tracing paper and a print of that tracing is presented on p. 129. The overall area is calculated as 1956 m². The orientation of the faces were measured and entered into the first program which worked out the values of pressure coefficient in all the zones; and stated the number of faces to be studied for each wind direction. The results of that program are presented on p. 130; data was also stored to be used by the next program. The areas of the zones have been measured by hand and have been entered; with the number of faces to be studied as required by the first program. The results of the second program are presented on p. 131 with the mean value of pressure coefficient and the roof load for every wind direction. Remember that the diagonal 'a' used in the calculation of wind speeds must be the maximum diagonal on the roof.

The orientation of the building to north is changed to 60° and the results are presented on pp. 132–133.

Height = 20 m

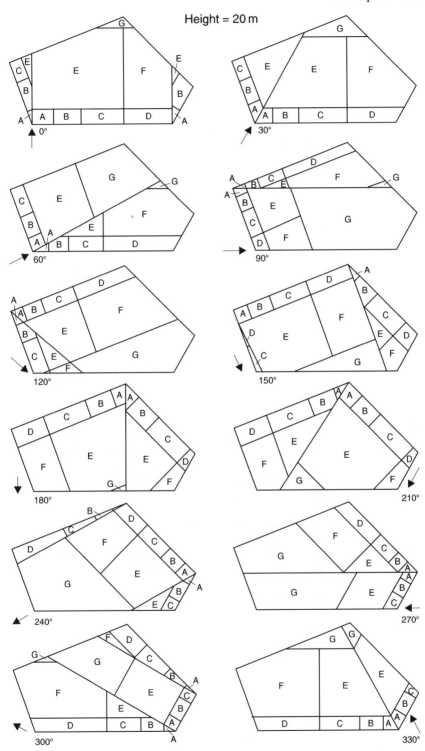

WD	Theta	A	B	C	D	E	F
1	0.0	−1.47	−1.25	−1.15	−1.15	−0.69	−0.71
1	65.0	−1.61	−1.11	−0.99	−0.54	−0.61	−0.35
1	62.0	−1.66	−1.19	−1.06	−0.60	−0.61	−0.39
2	30.0	−2.00	−1.70	−1.38	−1.03	−0.66	−0.67
2	35.0	−2.01	−1.66	−1.33	−0.98	−0.65	−0.63
3	60.0	−1.70	−1.24	−1.10	−0.64	−0.61	−0.42
3	5.0	−1.49	−1.28	−1.16	−1.15	−0.67	−0.71
4	90.0	−1.43	−0.75	−0.52	−0.24	−0.62	−0.20
4	25.0	−1.93	−1.67	−1.37	−1.08	−0.65	−0.69
4	69.0	−1.54	−1.00	−0.87	−0.46	−0.61	−0.28
5	55.0	−1.78	−1.34	−1.15	−0.72	−0.60	−0.47
5	39.0	−1.97	−1.60	−1.26	−0.93	−0.62	−0.59
6	85.0	−1.42	−0.75	−0.53	−0.25	−0.62	−0.19
6	9.0	−1.55	−1.34	−1.18	−1.15	−0.64	−0.70
6	74.0	−1.46	−0.87	−0.72	−0.37	−0.61	−0.22
7	21.0	−1.83	−1.60	−1.32	−1.11	−0.63	−0.70
7	44.0	−1.91	−1.51	−1.19	−0.87	−0.59	−0.55
8	51.0	−1.83	−1.40	−1.16	−0.78	−0.59	−0.50
8	14.0	−1.66	−1.45	−1.23	−1.14	−0.61	−0.70
8	88.0	−1.43	−0.75	−0.52	−0.24	−0.62	−0.20
9	81.0	−1.42	−0.77	−0.57	−0.28	−0.61	−0.19
9	16.0	−1.71	−1.49	−1.25	−1.14	−0.61	−0.70
9	58.0	−1.73	−1.28	−1.13	−0.68	−0.61	−0.44
10	90.0	−1.43	−0.75	−0.52	−0.24	−0.62	−0.20
10	46.0	−1.89	−1.47	−1.17	−0.85	−0.59	−0.53
10	28.0	−1.98	−1.69	−1.38	−1.05	−0.66	−0.68
11	60.0	−1.70	−1.24	−1.10	−0.64	−0.61	−0.42
11	76.0	−1.44	−0.83	−0.67	−0.33	−0.61	−0.20
11	2.0	−1.47	−1.26	−1.15	−1.15	−0.68	−0.71
12	30.0	−2.00	−1.70	−1.38	−1.03	−0.66	−0.67
12	32.0	−2.01	−1.69	−1.37	−1.01	−0.66	−0.66

Value of theta and Cp

Handbook example at 0 degrees

3 2 2 3 2 3 2 3 3 3 3 2

			Areas				
WD	A	B	C	D	E	F	G
0		-0.830		-5446			
	49	74	124	127	894	417	43
	11	53	49	17	0	0	0
	14	71	0	0	12	0	0
30		-0.829		-4562			
	29	65	103	139	547	547	106
	32	65	55	0	268	0	0
60		-0.554		-3003			
	9	34	71	150	80	514	5
	27	41	66	0	481	0	477
90		-0.417		-2357			
	0	0	0	0	0	0	0
	12	25	39	21	234	164	836
	4	20	39	109	22	410	20
120		-0.601		-3453			
	6	30	70	58	0	30	0
	20	38	70	115	379	590	550
150		-0.671		-4914			
	0	7	13	0	0	0	0
	32	49	81	92	751	458	208
	7	18	81	40	42	76	0
180		-0.836		-7633			
	35	74	119	91	682	249	6
	25	74	119	25	389	69	0
210		-0.750		-8490			
	16	66	113	100	212	276	0
	42	68	113	30	724	103	93
	0	0	0	0	0	0	0
240		-0.557		-7545			
	3	8	38	126	0	0	0
	21	40	66	63	439	334	679
	7	37	26	69	0	0	0
270		-0.462		-5921			
	0	0	0	0	0	0	0
	8	25	42	76	126	371	490
	13	25	27	0	246	0	506
300		-0.519		-5469			
	6	31	65	138	62	570	12
	5	17	48	67	0	36	0
	26	39	24	0	349	0	462
330		-0.789		-6029			
	24	54	89	137	465	656	107
	27	54	22	0	286	0	34

Values of roof areas, average Cp and load

Factor for load is 100

Handbook example 0 degrees

Value of 'a' used = 72.0

WD	Theta	A	B	C	D	E	F
1	60.0	−1.70	−1.24	−1.10	−1.15	−0.64	−0.42
1	76.0	−1.44	−0.83	−0.67	−0.33	−0.61	−0.20
1	2.0	−1.47	−1.26	−1.15	−1.15	−0.68	−0.71
2	30.0	−2.00	−1.70	−1.38	−1.03	−0.66	−0.67
2	32.0	−2.01	−1.69	−1.37	−1.01	−0.66	−0.66
3	0.0	−1.47	−1.25	−1.15	−1.15	−0.69	−0.71
3	65.0	−1.61	−1.11	−0.99	−0.54	−0.61	−0.35
3	62.0	−1.66	−1.19	−1.06	−0.60	−0.61	−0.39
4	30.0	−2.00	−1.70	−1.38	−1.03	−0.66	−0.67
4	35.0	−2.01	−1.66	−1.33	−0.98	−0.65	−0.63
5	60.0	−1.70	−1.24	−1.10	−0.64	−0.61	−0.42
5	5.0	−1.49	−1.28	−1.16	−1.15	−0.67	−0.71
6	90.0	−1.43	−0.75	−0.52	−0.24	−0.62	−0.20
6	25.0	−1.93	−1.67	−1.37	−1.08	−0.65	−0.69
6	69.0	−1.54	−1.00	−0.87	−0.46	−0.61	−0.28
7	55.0	−1.78	−1.34	−1.15	−0.72	−0.60	−0.47
7	39.0	−1.97	−1.60	−1.26	−0.93	−0.62	−0.59
8	85.0	−1.42	−0.75	−0.53	−0.25	−0.62	−0.19
8	9.0	−1.55	−1.34	−1.18	−1.15	−0.64	−0.70
8	74.0	−1.46	−0.87	−0.72	−0.37	−0.61	−0.22
9	21.0	−1.83	−1.60	−1.32	−1.11	−0.63	−0.70
9	44.0	−1.91	−1.51	−1.19	−0.87	−0.59	−0.55
10	51.0	−1.83	−1.40	−1.16	−0.78	−0.59	−0.50
10	14.0	−1.66	−1.45	−1.23	−1.14	−0.61	−0.70
10	88.0	−1.43	−0.75	−0.52	−0.24	−0.62	−0.20
11	81.0	−1.42	−0.77	−0.57	−0.28	−0.61	−0.19
11	16.0	−1.71	−1.49	−1.25	−1.14	−0.61	−0.70
11	58.0	−1.73	−1.28	−1.13	−0.68	−0.61	−0.44
12	90.0	−1.43	−0.75	−0.52	−0.24	−0.62	−0.20
12	46.0	−1.89	−1.47	−1.17	−0.85	−0.59	−0.53
12	28.0	−1.98	−1.69	−1.38	−1.05	−0.66	−0.68

Values of theta and Cp
Handbook example 60 degrees

3 2 3 2 2 3 2 3 2 3 3 3

WD	A	B	C	Areas D	E	F	G
0		-0.684		-4488			
	49	74	124	127	894	417	43
	11	53	49	17	0	0	0
	14	71	0	0	12	0	0
30		-0.833		-4581			
	29	65	103	139	547	547	106
	32	65	55	0	268	0	0
60		-0.651		-3530			
	9	34	71	150	80	514	5
	27	41	66	0	481	0	477
	0	0	0	0	0	0	0
90		-0.537		-3033			
	12	25	39	21	234	164	836
	4	20	39	109	22	410	20
120		-0.638		-3668			
	6	30	70	58	0	30	0
	20	38	70	115	379	590	550
150		-0.704		-5151			
	0	7	13	0	0	0	0
	32	49	81	92	751	458	208
	7	18	81	40	42	76	0
180		-0.774		-7064			
	35	74	119	91	682	249	6
	25	74	119	25	389	69	0
210		-0.623		-7052			
	16	66	113	100	212	276	0
	42	68	113	30	724	103	93
	0	0	0	0	0	0	0
240		-0.522		-7063			
	3	8	38	126	0	0	0
	21	40	66	63	439	334	679
270		-0.240		-3075			
	7	37	26	69	0	0	0
	0	0	0	0	0	0	0
	8	25	42	76	126	371	490
300		-0.606		-6379			
	13	25	27	0	246	0	506
	6	31	65	138	62	570	12
	5	17	48	67	0	36	0
330		-0.893		-6828			
	26	39	24	0	349	0	462
	24	54	89	137	465	656	107
	27	54	22	0	286	0	34

Values of roof areas, average Cp and load

Factor for load is 100

Handbook example 60 degrees

Value of 'a' used = 72.0

4

Background presentations

Article 1. Derivation of wind speed information

by M.J. Prior
Meteorological Office

Introduction

In order to assess design wind speeds, it was necessary to take account of the spatial variability of wind speed, linked to geographical location and local exposure. The accuracy with which this could be done was determined by the need for an acceptable method of calculation by Code users. A further requirement was to estimate those wind speeds that occur only rarely, and for this a novel approach was used giving direction and seasonal information as well as improved estimates of extreme wind speeds.

It was decided to follow the precedent set by CP3,[1] using a map for defining the geographical variation of a standardized extreme wind speed (the basic speed) and a set of factors to make the necessary allowances for the characteristics of the structure and its location.

Wind data

Following the development of reliable, continuously recording equipment (anemographs), a small network of anemograph stations was established by the Meteorological Office early this century. The 'official' network has grown so that it currently numbers about 130 stations; various instrumental improvements have also taken place.[2]

The wind data archived by the Meteorological Office are obtained from measurements made on masts or towers at Meteorological Stations, often

---

[1] BSI *Code of basic data for the design of buildings* BSI, 1972 chapter V. Loading. Part 2 Wind Loads.

[2] R.H. Collingbourne, Wind data available in the Meteorological Office', *Journal of Wind Engineering and Industrial Aerodynamics*, Vol 12, 1983, pp. 145–155; M.J. Prior and J.C. Dixon, 'Design Applications of the Meteorological Archives of Wind Data', Proceedings of the Wind Engineering Society Conference, Cambridge, September 1992.

on airfields, and at stations maintained by a variety of other bodies including research stations and the coastguard service.

When selecting a site for an anemograph, an exposure at a height of 10 m above ground in flat level terrain is preferred. Where this cannot be achieved, adjustments have to be made to the data to standardize them for comparison purposes. The main wind archive holds hourly values of the mean wind speed, mean wind direction, the maximum gust speed and its direction; values for the last 20 years are held on computer data sets.

Wind speed analysis

Introduction

Conventionally, estimation of the extreme wind climate in temperate regions has involved the analysis of a series of annual maximum wind speeds. The main disadvantage of this method is that many potentially useful wind speed values within each year are not used. For the preparation of the basic wind speed map in BS 6399, a new technique involving the maximum wind speed during every period of windy weather ('storm') was used. This approach greatly increased the data available for analysis and enabled the directional and seasonal characteristics of the UK wind climate to be examined.[3]

Fifty anemograph stations having a complete, or near complete, record during the period 1970–80 were selected; they are shown in Diagram 4.1. The majority of these were chosen for geographical location and standard exposure, but a few non-standard exposures were included to test the effectiveness of the analysis method.

A computer program was written to search the hourly mean wind speeds of each station and identify periods of at least 10 consecutive hours with an overall wind speed of at least 10 knots (5.1 m/s). Such periods were dubbed 'storms' and were associated with the passage of low pressure areas across the UK. The corresponding maximum hourly mean wind speeds occurring in each of 12 30° sectors (centred on 0°, 30°, etc.) were calculated. At the majority of the stations the average number of 'storms' per year was about 140.

Three types of extreme wind speed information were needed; a map of basic wind speeds (V_B), wind direction factors (S_d) and seasonal building factors (S_s).

Basic wind speed

Extreme value analyses were performed on the 'storm' maxima, irrespective of direction, to produce estimates of the speeds having a probability of 0.02 of being exceeded at least once a year (this is equivalent to an average frequency of occurrence of once in 50 years, or a 'return period' of 50 years).

---

[3] N.J. Cook and M.J. Prior, 'Extreme wind climate of the United Kingdom', *Journal of Wind Engineering and Industrial Aerodynamics*, Vol 26, 1987, pp. 371–389.

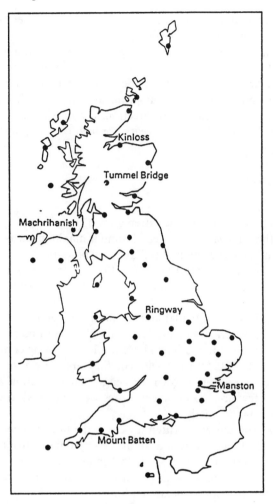

Diagram 4.1

These basic hourly wind speeds were plotted on a map of the UK at the relevant station locations. Before isotachs could be drawn, allowances had to be made for any nonstandard sites. For example, speeds at coastal locations facing the prevailing westerly winds in order to standardize them to open, level country terrain. Similarly speeds at non-standard heights were adjusted to represent speeds 10 m above the ground. Corrections were also made for altitude, so that the map represented conditions at mean sea level. The anemograph stations used in the 'storms' search were all in the UK, so to assist with interpolation for sites on the Isle of Man and western coasts it was necessary to estimate isotachs over Eire. This estimation was done by comparing 'storm' results for Northern Ireland with a basic (gust) wind map for Eire prepared by the Irish Meteorological Service.

Directional analysis

Extreme value analyses were then performed on the direction wind speeds maxima, to produce speeds with an annual probability of exceedence of 0.02. Ratios of the sectorial extremes to the all-direction extreme were calculated for all stations. After correction for site exposure, the directional characteristics of extreme winds showed no significant variation with location, with the strongest winds blowing from directions from south-west to west. This enabled one national set of directional factors to be proposed (S_d).

Seasonal analysis

Lastly the overall 'storm' maxima (irrespective of direction) were analysed for each month, using a technique similar to that used for the annual analyses. The seasonal characteristics of strong winds showed no significant variation across the UK so again one set of factors could be adopted (S_s). The highest extreme winds are expected in the mid-winter whilst the least windy period is between June and August with extreme winds that are only about 65 per cent of the winter values.

Site wind speeds

Introduction

When obtaining a design wind speed for a specific site (V_s), the calculation process restores the local features of the site altitude, terrain roughness, topography and height above ground that were removed when the standardized 'basic' wind speed map was prepared. Other adjustments allow for directionality and exposure period. The starting point is the basic wind speed (V_b) for the general area in which the site lies.

Adjustments for altitude and direction

The first step was to increase the basic wind speed for the site's altitude above sea level using the factor S_a; this changes the wind speed by 10 per cent for every 100 m above sea level and has been derived from the study reported in Caton, 1976.[4] This correction allows only for the effect of large-scale topography; local features such as hills and cliffs are taken into account by the topography factor (see 'Adjustment for topography' below).

If the design is directionally dependent, the direction factor (S_d) as discussed in 'Directional analysis' is then applied for the relevant 30° sector. This reflects the fact that (in the absence of any localized exposure effects), the risk of strong winds is lower from those directions with an easterly component than from those with a westerly one.

---

[4] P.G.F. Caton, Maps of hourly-mean Wind Speed over the United Kingdom 1965–1973, Climatological Memo No 79, Meteorological Office, 1976.

Adjustment for period of exposure

The factor S_s was derived in order to alter the annual risk of exceedence. For example, for designs needing a high degree of security, such as a building for the nuclear power industry, an annual probability of exceedence lower than the standard value of 0.02 would be required. In contrast, if the structure is to be exposed for a limited period, for example a temporary structure to be used only in the summer, then the seasonal building factor (S_s), as discussed in 'Seasonal analysis' above is applied for the month(s) in question.

Adjustment for terrain and height above ground

The roughness of the earth's surface affects both the mean wind speed in the lower atmosphere and its turbulent characteristics. Speeds are higher over smooth surfaces, such as the sea, and lower in built-up areas, where conditions are more turbulent. By defining three terrain categories, adjustments can be made to the 'basic' speed to account for the influence of the terrain upwind of the site. These categories are:

Sea   – for sites offshore, on windward coasts and close to lakes extending at least 10 km upwind.

Country   – for rural sites with no shelter to those with occasional obstructions such as trees, walls and buildings.

Town   – sites in cities and suburban areas, provided the plan area of buildings upwind within at least 1 km is at least 8 per cent.

Since the change in wind speed as air flows from one terrain category to another is not instantaneous, but spreads upwards into the lower atmosphere, the distance of the site to the terrain change upwind (the 'fetch') needs to be taken into account. This principle is illustrated in Diagram 4.2, for wind passing from a smooth terrain to a rougher one (e.g. from country to town).

   The necessary adjustments are made by a series of fetch and turbulence factors that vary with the distance of the site to the terrain category change and with the exposed height of the structure. Other than when the site is in a town itself, shelter from any town(s) upwind has not been allowed for in the Code. The Building Research Establishment micro-computer program STRONGBLOW[5] can be used to allow for such effects, as well as those of a wider selection of terrain types.

Adjustment for topography

The Altitude Correction Factor S_a corrects for the general level of the site above sea level, but does not allow for local features, such as hills, that can significantly alter the wind speed. Accelerations occur near the summits of hills and the tops of cliffs, whereas decelerations occur in valleys and at the bases of cliffs. In the Code, these effects need to be considered when the

---

[5] N.J. Cook, B.W. Smith and M.V. Husband, STRONGBLOW: Users Manual, BRE Microcomputer Package, Garston, 1985.

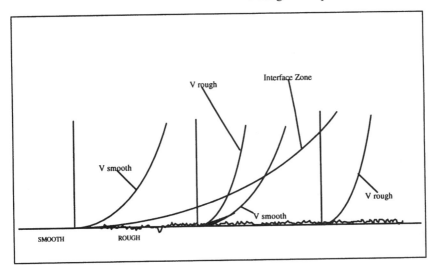

Diagram 4.2

average slope of the ground within 1 km of the site (or in the relevant direction) exceeds 1 in 20 (5 per cent or 0.05).

When slopes are between 1 in 20 and 1 in 3, wind accelerates up the upwind slope to a maximum at the summit or crest. The effect varies with height and is greatest near the ground. Downwind of the highest point, the wind slows down again. When the upwind slope exceeds about 1 in 3, the wind flow separates from the surface ahead of the slope and jumps to a point just below the summit or crest. The boundary of the separated region forms an effective slope equal to the critical value of 1 in 3, so that the flow over the feature is the same as that for the critical value. The topography factor S_h therefore varies according to the shape and average slope of the feature, the position of the site relative to the summit or crest and with the height above ground level. It is greatest close to the summit or crest of features with a slope of 1 in 3 or more, where it has a value of 0.6 (equivalent to a speed-up of 60 per cent compared to conditions well upwind of the feature).

The design rules used for S_h were derived from comparisons of results from wind tunnel models with field measurements and confirm the result from theory[6] that changes in mean wind speed over gentle topography are proportional to the upwind slope.

Adjustments for size of structure

The basic wind values (V_b) are hourly wind speeds. However, for static structures the appropriate peak ('gust') speed that will envelop the structure or component to produce the maximum loading has to be chosen.

---

[6] P.S. Jackson and J.C.R. Hunt, Turbulent wind flow over a low hill, *Quarterly Journal of the Royal Meteorological Society*, Vol 101, pp. 929–955.

Comparisons over several terrain types of the peak speeds measured over time intervals from a few seconds to several minutes with that averaged over an hour have led to factors adjusting peak wind speed averaging times. For example, the 2-second gust speed in a hour in an open level situation is typically 1.6 times the mean for the hour.

The averaging time varies with the design application, being a few seconds for small components such as tiles or glazing units but several minutes for whole structures of considerable height or length. This variation in averaging time is included using the factor g_t which depends upon the exposed height and diagonal length of the loaded area. When multiplied by the site turbulence factors, the resulting factor is equivalent to that for the averaging time adjustments described above.

Concluding remarks

The calculations used in the preparation and application of the Code are essentially concerned with two processes. The first is the analysis of the recorded wind speeds to give 'basic' wind speed values, standardized for frequency of occurrence, altitude, height above ground, terrain and topography. Important by-products are the directional and seasonal extreme wind speed information.

The second process considers the site and the structure that is to be placed there, restores the local features removed in the first process and includes design characteristics such as exposure period and directionality. These processes may be thought of as two 'equations', as shown in Diagram 4.3.

Further information on the assessment of wind loads using the methods of BS 6399 is given in *BRE Digest* and Cook, 1985.[7]

Wind Speed Extremes Anemographs 1,2.......49,50	-	Station Characteristics i.e. altitude height above ground local terrain local topography	=	Basic Wind Speed Map
Basic Wind Speed Value	+ Site Characteristics i.e. altitude terrain topography	+ Design Characteristics i.e. direction exposure period structure size	=	Design Wind Speed Value

Diagram 4.3

[7] BRE, The assessment of wind loads, *BRE Digest* 346, 7 parts 1989; N.J. Cook, *The Designer's Guide to Wind Loading of Building Structures* Part 1 Background, Damage Survey, Wind Data and Structural Classification, Butterworths, 1985.

Article 2. General aspects of wind flow around buildings

Introduction

In this article the general aspects of aerodynamics as they affect the flow around buildings will be enunciated. In many instances the situations will be simplified so that they are comprehensible to the reader and in so doing they may lose a degree of academic rigour; this is inescapable in a document of this kind.

The approaching wind

The usual determining feature of the wind is its speed. This simple statement is more complex than it appears because the wind speed, even at a location, is continually changing both in magnitude and direction. So a few introductory remarks about the wind may not come amiss.

In the first place the wind is created by the differential heating of the air by the sun. Strangely all the energy from the sun of frequencies which can be absorbed by the air is absorbed more than 50 km above ground level. The rest of the energy comes through the atmosphere undiminished and impinges on clouds or on the earth's surface, by which it is absorbed. Those surfaces then re-transmit the energy at different frequencies, including those which can be absorbed by the air. It is for this reason that, although the heating is caused by the sun, the temperature of the air decreases for approximately the first 10 000 m above the surface of the earth (sometimes called the thermosphere). The reflective nature of surfaces differ, most notably those on land and water and this is why there are sea breezes at the coast, because the storage and reflective capacity of land and water is different so that, in the changeovers between day/night/day there is a time lag between the emission of the different surfaces creating the sea breezes.

Variations of wind speed with time is often called 'turbulence'. It fact there are two different scales of time involved. The larger or 'macro meteorological' are produced by a variety of causes varying from sun spots with cycles of about 11 to 13 years for intense activity, through winter/summer effects of about 6 months, through weather systems with a mean period of about 3 days, to the period of about 8 hours which are caused by the day/ night heating effects. All these are lumped together by the wind engineer and are described as of 'meteorological origin'. The smaller, called the 'micro meteorological' have periods of less than 1 hour and are imposed on the wind created by the above effects blowing over the roughness of the earth's surface and protuberances thereon.

Because the two scales and the mechanisms which are the causes are different, they are said to be 'uncorrelated', that is to say they are produced by quite different causes and so a high value from one cause can be associated with any value from the other. The dividing line is an averaging time of 1 hour and this is called the 'spectral gap'.

It is now possible to conduct completely separate statistical analyses in the two regimes. In the first regime the macro meteorological data ends up in Codes like BS 6399 as values of the 'hourly average wind speed' which have the probability of 1/50 of being exceeded in any one year (these are presented in the form of 'basic wind speeds' on a map, because they are geographically variable). They are adjusted to 'site' values by altitude, direction and seasonal factors. The 'probability' factor in the adjustment from basic to site values is the statistical aspect. The spectrum of these winds is not of interest to the structural engineer so will be ignored here, and the probability aspect of the magnitude has been calculated using 'extreme value analysis'. The 'parent distribution', from which the extremes have been derived, is of interest in discussing the wind environment of the site and is usually presented in the form of a 'Weibull distribution'.

In the second regime, the variations of the micro meteorological type, which are often referred to as 'turbulence', have their own statistical analyses. These take the form of 'spectra' and 'probability distributions'. To explain the effects of turbulence it is convenient to think of the micro meteorological turbulence as composed of an infinite number of eddies of different sizes and orientations. In this regime both spectra and distribution are important because eddies in different ranges of sizes react differently with the building. In addition, because this turbulence has been caused by the wind blowing over the rough land, the nature of the boundary layer of the flow, that is to say the velocity profile, is also important.

Thus the three aspects of the approaching wind which have a major effect on its reaction with buildings are of the micro meteorological type, the macro meteorological effects only affect its magnitude.

Effect of wind characteristics on the flow around a building

The reason why the velocity profile (the variation of wind speed with height) is important is because it produces three-dimensional effects. Over a flat open field the atmospheric boundary layer, like a boundary layer on any surface, has zero velocity at the surface and increases to a free stream value (called gradient wind speed in the atmospheric boundary layer). In the atmospheric boundary layer in a town (again like any boundary layer on a surface with many tall protuberances), the velocity reaches zero at the ground (because this is a boundary condition), but the velocity profile within the houses is not a continuation of the velocity profile above the houses. In fact, if the velocity profile above the houses were extrapolated, it would give a zero value of wind speed at a considerable distance above the ground; this distance is called the 'zero plane displacement'. This concept is important because the shape of the velocity profile can be related in a mathematical sense to the ground roughness (either mathematically by making assumptions, the log law, or by empirical fitting of expressions to the measured profile, the power law) These representations only apply above the height of the houses and all tables of wind speed in this Code derive therefrom, so it is important to know their imaginary starting point. Within the houses the velocity profile can be anything, depending upon individual houses and their spacing. In this Code the term 'zero plane displacement' is shortened to 'displacement height'. Consequently, to know the value of wind speed at a height above the ground from the tables in this Code, it is necessary to know the height above this level.

Consider the wind blowing normal to a building in a flat open site, shown in Diagram 4.4. On the front face of the building the wind will be brought to rest along a vertical line which is the division between the wind flowing to left and right; this is called the 'stagnation line'. As the wind is brought to rest, its velocity energy is converted into pressure, and, as the wind speed in the atmosphere increases with height, so a pressure gradient develops along the stagnation line. This pressure gradient causes the air to move down the face of the building, causing a redistribution of pressure around the building. At first glance it would appear that the air would move downwards from the top of the building, but, because there is a very large negative pressure over the top of the building, there is a dividing point at about 70 per cent of the height of the building with the air above that point flowing upwards and that below flowing downwards. This redistribution of air within the site is of importance in establishing the pressures over the whole building.

There are three ranges of turbulent frequencies which affect the flow round a building and thus its wind loading.

The very large eddies, which encompass the whole face of a building, will affect the flow in the form of a change of either wind speed or direction over the whole of the face at the same time, so this change appears like a series of quasi-static flow patterns over the face and is

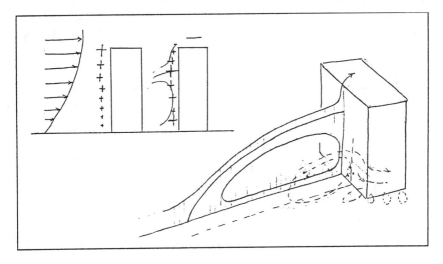

Diagram 4.4

accounted for by a fluctuating pressure at a location, fluctuations which do not exactly correspond to the variations of the u-component of turbulence in the approaching wind.

The very small eddies (compared to the size of the building) appear as wiggles of the streamlines flowing over the building. Often these can have no effect except a rapid uncorrelated fluctuation of the pressure at all locations, without changing the overall flow pattern and therefore the basic pressure distribution. However there is an exception to this and that is in the zone immediately after separation (see Diagram 4.5).

At sharp corners the flow cannot turn instantaneously through a sharp angle, so it 'separates' from the surface, possibly returning to 'reattach' at a future point should the face be long enough. The presence of very small scale turbulence, because it enhances local mixing, causes reattachment to occur sooner. Thus the curvature of the 'shear layer' which bounds the 'separation bubble' is greater, producing a lower pressure (increased suction) within the bubble, and therefore at all locations within the bubble. Thus the low pressure in the bubble is increased and the length of the bubble is shortened by the very small scale turbulence. Also because these effects alter the basic flow pattern (the size of the bubble), they affect the basic value of pressure over a greater region than that of only the bubble.

The eddies of a size in a range about the size of the building have an overall effect on the general flow pattern around the building because, at a given instant, they affect different parts of the building differently and there is then a secondary flow established consequent on this variation which must be taken into account.

Because turbulence in distinct ranges of frequency affects the overall flow patterns around buildings, and it is essential that all are included in any wind tunnel study (their omission is one of the reasons why the early data on the pressure distribution around buildings obtained from 'aircraft type, turbulence free' wind tunnels was inaccurate). To ensure that the three ranges are modelled, it is usual to model the entire spectrum. This is the reason for Annex A in the Code.

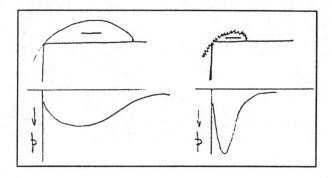

Diagram 4.5

Because the speed of the approaching wind is changing with time (turbulence), the pressure this wind produces on the surfaces of a building will also change with time, the changes being linked or 'correlated'. This applies directly to the front faces of the building where the wind impacts directly on the surface. On the side faces, when there are separations at the corner, the fluctuations of pressure are governed more by the turbulence generated by the separation than by the turbulence in the approaching wind, which is now separated from the flow over the surface of the side faces by the shear layer sprouting from the separation point. On these faces the fluctuations of pressure are said to be 'uncorrelated' from the fluctuations in the approaching wind. This is a slightly different meaning for 'correlation'; it means here that the peaks of the fluctuating pressure do not occur at the same time (or simultaneously) at two different points on the building.

The meaning of correlation

When describing the different scales of fluctuations of the wind it was stated that the 'macro meteorological' and the 'micro meteorological' scales of turbulence were 'uncorrelated' because the scales and the causes were so different. This is a correct meaning of the term.

However, another correct meaning is applied to fluctuating wind speeds and pressures. When the fluctuating pressure is measured at two points on the surface of a building, then a range of peaks of pressure will occur on both, but not necessarily simultaneously. If the points are close together, then the peaks could be very similar but occur at one point a short time after occurring at the other point. In which case the simultaneous pressure at both points would be slightly lower than the peak value. As the distance apart of the points increases, the peak values will get further apart, but it is now possible that the peak at one point could occur simultaneously with the next peak at the other point. Thus, when the fluctuating pressure on a surface is integrated to produce a fluctuating load, account must be taken of this time warp. This is considered in practice by studying the 'spectra' of the pressure. It is assumed that low frequencies are the manifestation of large eddies and will occur simultaneously over a large area, and high frequency fluctuations will occur over a small area. The simultaneous pressure over a given area is therefore the sum of the effects of all the eddies from the very largest down to a critical size of eddy depending upon the size of the area.

Difference between face and overall loads

So far only the flow on a face has been considered. The shear layer mentioned above is the freely flowing boundary layer from the face upwind. Recent measurement has shown that there is no correlation between the fluctuations on either side of the shear layer. It would therefore be conservative to calculate the peak gust loads on two faces (based on the turbulence of the oncoming stream) *separated by a shear layer* and simply add components of the loads on the faces to get a value for the overall load in a given direction. If the flow is onto the corner of a building, then there is no shear layer separating the flow on the two faces forming the corner: in that case, the pressure would be correlated and be related to the turbulence in the approaching stream.

The dilemma is this. Values of pressure averaged over a given time which have a stated probability of exceedence have been measured in a wind tunnel and have been divided by the dynamic pressure in the tunnel averaged over the same time and with the same probability of exceedence. This gives a true Gust Pressure Coefficient. Consider two locations, one on one face and the other on another separated from the first by a shear layer. In the wind tunnel investigation the measurements have been taken in a situation in which there is a shear layer separating their faces, and are both related to the dynamic pressure upwind of the building. The peak pressures on the two faces do occur, because they have been measured, the difficulty is that they were not measured simultaneously.

For the calculation of overall loads, in the Standard method this dilemma was resolved by multiplying the overall load calculated by the integration of face loads by 0.85. This factor was derived from a few cases when forces and pressures were measured in a wind tunnel investigation.

For the calculation of overall loads in the Directional method the dilemma is resolved differently for the calculation of overall loads. It is assumed that the pressure coefficients on a 'windward' face are subject to the fluctuations of the oncoming wind and are converted into values of pressure by the peak dynamic pressure based on the diagonal of the frontal area. On all 'leeward' faces (those separated by a shear layer from the approaching wind), it is assumed that the pressure coefficient averaged over the whole surface is constant and is converted into a value of pressure by the same dynamic pressure. The non-correlation of the two pressures is again accounted for by the factor 0.85.

The calculation of panel and face loads is straightforward because no parts of the face or panel are uncorrelated from other parts of the same face.

Use of pressure coefficients

The data supplied in the Code are to apply to full size buildings, but these data have been obtained from wind tunnel measurements. How can this be justified?

Buckingham's Pi Theorem in dimensional analysis states that if a 'dependent' quantity (say the pressure on a building) is dependent on N independent quantities (air density, wind speed etc.) then a non-dimensional expression of the dependent quantity applies to all 'geometrically similar' bodies provided that $N-3$ non-dimensional quantities (containing *all* the independent quantities) are the same.

In the present case the dependent variable is the pressure p and the independent variables are in two groups, the first concerning the wind and the second the building. In the first group are the air density (ρ), wind speed (V), viscosity of air (μ), the change of density with pressure ($d\rho/dp$): in the second group are size (L) and orientation of the building (α).

Thus, with $N = 6$, there shall be three non-dimensional groups

$$p/(1/2\rho V^2) = f\,(\alpha, \rho\,V\,L/\mu, V^2 \times d\rho/dp)$$

where
$p/(1/2\rho\,V^2)$ is called the pressure coefficient
α is the orientation
$\rho VL/\mu$ is called the 'Reynolds number' and is the ratio of the inertia force on an element of air flowing past the building to the viscous.
$V^2 d\rho/dp$ is the square of the Mach number.

There are other independent quantities which have minor effects and produce other numbers, but they have very little effect on this case.

The Mach number is unimportant provided that the wind speed is small compared to the speed of sound (330 m/s at normal temperatures).

The Reynolds number, together with surface roughness and the turbulence in the air, affects the 'separation' of the flow from a surface and is thus a very important parameter. However, because ρ and μ for air depend upon temperature and cannot be adjusted in most wind tunnels, to get the same Reynolds number for model and full-scale tests, the product $V \times L$ would have to be the same. This would mean for a 1/100 model, the test would have to be conducted at 100 times the wind speed. Not only is that impractical, but then the Mach number criterion would be breached.

To resolve this impasse, a study of the effects of Reynolds on buildings is made and it is found that for 'sharp-edged' buildings, separation takes place at the sharp corner irrespective of the value of the Reynolds number. It is therefore possible to test sharp-edged buildings in an atmospheric wind tunnel and obtain realistic results.

For curved buildings the situation is not completely lost because it is found that there are regions of Reynolds number where the results are independent of Reynolds number. Separation depends upon the state of the boundary layer on the body. If this state is 'laminar' or 'fully turbulent' (which are defined by Reynolds number, the roughness of the surface and the turbulence of the approaching wind) Reynolds number is relatively unimportant, but the surface roughness of the building is important in the turbulent case. In between there is a 'critical' region where Reynolds number is all important.

Because of their size, most structures and all buildings have fully turbulent boundary layers, so that, even for curved buildings, provided that they are studied in fully turbulent conditions in the wind tunnel, and the surface roughness is correctly scaled, then wind tunnel data apply.

It thus transpires that, for sharp-edged buildings, identity between values of pressure coefficient in the wind tunnel and at full-scale occur for geometrically similar buildings at the same orientation. Even on curved walled buildings data can apply but extreme care must be exercised in their application.

Areas on faces

In general in the tables of values of pressure coefficient the faces of buildings are divided into zones, the reason for this derives from the argument above on the effect of wind characteristics on the flow around a building. On side faces the 'separation bubble' is obviously one zone, the 'reattachment area' is another and the majority of the face a third. However it is possible to conceive a fourth, that at the end of the face when the wind is accelerating over the end of the face into the wake behind the building.

When the wind blows directly onto a face of a building, there is no separation on the face and fewer areas are possible. This also applies to the face of a building completely immersed in the wake of the building. Thus 'front' and 'rear' faces of buildings often have only one value of pressure coefficient associated with them.

When the wind blows at an angle to the normal from a face, then the zones described above have to be divided along the length of the building and separation zones added to the edge of the face now receiving approaching wind. Thus the number of zones in the Directional method is increased.

Special zones

There are certain special zones about which some mention should be made.

Contrary to general feeling, the zone at the front of a side face which has the highest suction is not that either at the top of the building, or that opposite the 70 per cent stagnation point, but is a location much lower. This is because the wind which is diverted downwards has to escape around the building. As the wind descends, it senses the ground before it is reached and begins to turn some 25 per cent of the height of the building from the ground. Here not only local wind but that brought down is turning round the corner and, at some point like 25 per cent it reaches a maximum, giving maximum suctions in this region. This is why the division by parts rule is not allowed for the calculation of cladding loads and why the instructions given for the application of the 'division-by-parts' rule must be followed meticulously.

Article 3. Wind sensitive buildings: Buildings which respond dynamically

Introduction

This Code specifically excludes buildings which respond dynamically to the wind; these are called 'wind sensitive' buildings. In the next section a layman explanation of the reason is given and in the following section a scientific reason is given.

However, a wind sensitive building does not usually have wind sensitive cladding, so that the cladding loads can still be calculated by the data presented in the Code.

Layman's arguments

Consider a child's swing: if you give a small push and maintain hold of the seat, then the swing will deflect a small amount. However, if you give the same push, but leave go of the swing, and give the swing the same push every time the seat reaches its nearest point to you, the amplitude of the swing will increase with each push.

With time the increase in amplitude after each push will decrease until eventually the amplitude will stay constant. This is called the 'limit state' condition. This will occur when the energy that you apply to the swing in each cycle is equal to the energy that is dissipated in damping in each cycle. In the case of the swing the damping is at the pivots and an aerodynamic drag of the seat and its occupant if any. The amplitude of the swing is a 'great many' times larger than the deflection of the seat when you applied the same load to it and maintained that load constant by holding the swing. The numerical value of the 'great many' depends mainly on the damping and only to a very small extent upon the actual load applied.

If the pivots of the swing were replaced by flexures, and the swing were turned upside down, you would have the situation of a building. The damping would now be the damping throughout the whole of the building not just at the flexures, still including aerodynamic damping. Damping depends upon movement, the greater the movement, the greater the damping. The ultimate amplitude would be that which would dissipate by damping (friction) in every cycle of oscillation the energy applied to the building in that cycle. The *stresses* in the flexures would be that caused by the *deflection* of the building, that is to say its *ultimate amplitude*. This is dependent more on the damping of the building than the load applied.

Like the swing, although dependent on the applied load, the ultimate amplitude could be many times the static deflection, with the ultimate stresses many times the static stresses. Fitting a number to the 'many times' is the difficulty, no, the impossibility without a full dynamic analysis.

The problem in the past has been that the Code did not give any guidance regarding the dynamic nature of a building. The present Code does, in that it allows the quasi-static approach to be used if the 'many times' is less than

1.25. What is more, it gives expressions by which the 'many times', which is now defined by the 'dynamic magnification factor' (the 'many times' is equal to 1 plus the dynamic magnification factor), can be evaluated for conventional buildings.

Scientific arguments

The simplest comparable dynamic system is a Mass connected to earth by a spring and a damper. The systems shown in Diagram 4.6 and the equation of motion of the mass is

$$m\ddot{x} + c\dot{x} + kx = \text{Applied Force} = f$$

where m is the mass, c is the damping, k is the stiffness and x is the displacement. Or, of greater relevance, $m\ddot{x}$ is the inertia force on the mass, $c\dot{x}$ is the damping force and kx is the stiffness force.

If a sinusoidal force is applied; that is to say

$$f = f_0 \sin(\omega t + \varphi)$$

and the deflection is also assumed to be sinusoidal, so that

$$x = x_0 \sin(\omega t)$$

and if the Argand Diagram is plotted (see Diagram 4.7), it can be seen that, if the excitation is at the natural frequency of the system ($\omega = \omega_0$), φ becomes $\pi/2$ and the equation of Motion breaks into two parts, viz.:

$$c\dot{x} = \text{Applied Force} = f$$

$$\text{and } m\ddot{x} + kx = 0$$

These are mathematical expressions of the statements made in the section on laymen's arguments.

The next problem is to relate the simple mass/damper/spring system to a complex building. This is done by the 'generalised mode displacement system' developed within the aerospace industry. It is assumed that any one

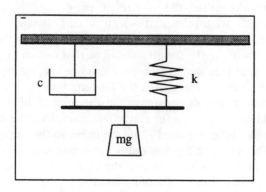

Diagram 4.6

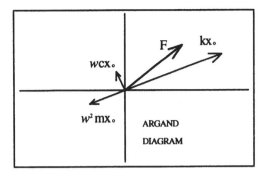

Diagram 4.7

mode of vibration of the building is unrelated from any other, in other words, that an oscillation in one mode does not interfere with a different mode of oscillation. The building is said to have an infinite number of 'modes' of oscillation, each of which is associated with a particular frequency and with a special shape of oscillation (called the 'mode shape'). For every 'mode' the values of mass, damping and stiffness are replaced by a 'generalised mass', 'generalised damping', 'generalised stiffness' and 'generalised force': the word mode is usually dropped from what was originally 'mode generalised mass' etc.

The deflection of any part of the building at an instant t during the oscillation in the ith mode $\{x_i(l,t)\}$ is related to a generalised displacement $\{x_i(t)\}$ and the mode shape $\{\mu_i(l)\}$ by the expression;

$$x_i(l, t) = X_i(t) \times \mu_i(l).$$

It will be seen that this procedure has separated the deflection which is time and position dependent into two variables, the generalised displacement in the ith mode, which is only time dependent and the mode shape in the ith mode which is only position dependent.

The generalised equation of motion in the ith mode is the same as the original equation except that the lower case letters have been replaced by the capitals if the generalised notation in the ith mode. Thus

$$Mi\ dX_i^2/dt^2 = 2(M_i \times K_i)^{0.5} \times dX_i/dt + K_i\ X_i = F_i(t)$$

$$\text{and} \qquad \omega_i = K_i/M_i.$$

The way the 'generalisation' is performed is illustrated here by a description of the generalised mass. The work done by the generalised inertia force $(M_i\ddot{x}_i)$ in a generalised displacement dX_i in the ith mode is equal to the integration up the building of the work done by a strip of the building $(m\ddot{x})$ moving through a virtual displacement dx_i in the ith mode. Thus

$$\int\limits_0^L (m\ddot{x})_i \, dx_i \, dl = \int\limits_0^L m(l)\mu_i^2(l)\ddot{X}_i \, dX_i \, dl = M_i \, \ddot{X}_i \, dX_i$$

$$\text{or} \qquad M_i = \int\limits_0^L m(l)\mu_i^2(l)dl$$

where $m(l)$ is the Mass per unit length at position l. The other generalised quantities are derived in the same way.

The evaluation of the frequency and mode shape of each mode, which is required to evaluate the generalised quantities, is usually carried out by the 'lumped mass method' which will be found in many textbooks on the subject or in Volume 4 of the ESDU Wind Engineering Series.

Thus the statement, which was originally made about the simple mass/damper/spring system, can be applied to the complex building in each of its modes of oscillation separately.

Cladding loads

It has been the purpose of this article to give sufficient background so that any user of the Code can understand why the calculation of overall loads on wind sensitive buildings are excluded from the Code, this is contained in the two previous sections.

The reasoning on overall loads is that the structure of the building stores energy from one cycle of oscillation to another. The same can obviously not be said of the cladding loads and their fixings, which occur instantaneously with the applied load and are directly related thereto. There can obviously be no restriction on the application of Code loads to cladding items, irrespective to the nature of the building. If cladding items are integral with some larger structural item, then it is possible that the stresses in the large structural item could be increased if the larger item can store energy. The above arguments should allow the reader to assess each situation correctly.

There is always the possibility that individual cladding items, like large sheets of glass can oscillate within their fixings. If this is possible, then even a single sheet of glass can store energy from one cycle to another and have its own dynamic magnification factor. The question here is simple and requires the verification that the lowest natural frequency of panels within their fixings is greater than any found in the atmosphere. *Usually* a minimum value above 5 Hz will ensure this requirement, but there are special instances when higher frequencies can be generated by the building, frequencies which are not present in the atmospheric winds, so this limit is not sacrosanct.

Article 4. Introduction to the statistics required

For a full appreciation of the Code a little understanding of statistics is required. In the paragraphs that follow an attempt will be made to explain sufficient statistics for this to be achieved without going into the fundamentals.

In wind loading where the magnitude of all parameters varies with time, data have to be presented which can be used in calculations. In the following paragraphs, the statistical methods used will be explained in reference to a fluctuating pressure.

The fluctuating pressure on a part of a building can be defined as composed of a mean part and a fluctuating part; thus

$$p(t) = \bar{p} + p'(t)$$

where $p(t)$ is the pressure which fluctuates with time, $\bar{p}$ is the mean pressure and $p'(t)$ is the purely fluctuating part of the pressure.

The mean part can be applied to the building statically. But more will be said of this below.

Two different aspects of the fluctuating part $p'(t)$ can be described; the first aspect defines its magnitude and the second its variation with time.

The simplest way to quantify the fluctuating part is to define either a 'standard deviation', which is equal to the root mean square of the fluctuating part (the root mean square of the pressure should be the root mean square of the whole pressure, mean plus fluctuating parts, but the two definitions are sometimes confused). Thus the standard deviation of the pressure is

$$\sigma^2(p) = \frac{1}{N}\sum_{i=1}^{N} p_i'^2(t) = \frac{1}{T}\int_0^T p'^2(t)dt.$$

However, this is not the most useful value to describe the magnitude of the fluctuating pressure. So we will start again.

Consider a new concept, called the 'probability density function', usually denoted by $p(p)$ defined in the following way. If instantaneous values of pressure are measured at 'N' regular intervals throughout a sample and if the range of pressure from maximum to minimum is divided into a series of 'boxes', it is possible to count up the number of times the value of pressure lies within the limits defining every box, say 'n_i' in box i. The probability density function $p(p_i)$ is equal to n_i/N for the box whose central value was p_i. If the size of individual boxes were reduced to zero and their number increased to infinity, the probability density function would be a continuous function of pressure.

The value of the probability density function $p(p)$ can be integrated from minus infinity to a given value of pressure, say p_a, to obtain a cumulative distribution function $P(p_a)$, which is the probability that the value of pressure is less than the value p_a, thus

$$P(p_a) = \int_{-\infty}^{P_a} p(p)dp.$$

or sometimes it is more convenient to define a slightly different cumulative distribution function $Q(p_a)$ which represents the probability that the value of pressure is above a given value p_a, thus

$$Q(p_a) = \int_{P_a}^{\infty} p(p)dp,$$

by definition

$$P(p_a) + Q(p_a) = 1.$$

Looking at this backwards, it is now possible to state a value of pressure, p_a, which has a given value $(Q(p_a))$ of being exceeded provided that the shape of the probability density function curve is known. From a set of readings it is possible determine the value which has a given probability of being exceeded without knowing the shape of the function.

This immediately introduces a concept with which the purist would have started; the size of the sample. Obviously if the sample, the number of readings, were very small, then the statistics would mean nothing. A limiting length of sample called the 'statistical length' must be defined. This is a length of sample out of a 'population' (an infinitely long sample) from which the statistical values derived would be the same. In all wind engineering situations this would never happen, so the practical engineer has to be satisfied with accepting 'weakly stationary' data. For this the mean value and the value of the standard deviation from a sample taken anywhere within the population must be the same as the values taken from any other position within the population.

It is simple to show that

$$\sigma^2 = \int_{-\infty}^{\infty} p^2 p(p)dp.$$

So much for defining the magnitude of the pressure.

To give a measure of the time content, it is common practice to invert 'time' and talk about '1/time' or 'frequency'.

By Fourrier analysis it is possible to break down any fluctuating pressure into its fundamental sine and cosine fluctuations. Thus;

$$p(t) = \int_0^{\infty} [I_1(n) \cos 2\pi nt + I_2(n) \sin 2\pi nt] dn$$

$$\sigma_p^2 = \frac{1}{T} \int_0^T p^2(t)dt$$

$$\sigma_p^2 = \frac{1}{T} \int_0^T \int_0^{\infty} [I_1(n) \cos 2\pi nt + I_2(n) \sin 2\pi nt]^2 \, dndt$$

$$\sigma_p^2 = \frac{1}{T} \int_0^T \int_0^\infty \{[I_1^2(n) + I_2^2(n)]/2\} dn\, dt$$

We can now define a 'spectral density function' $(S_{pp}(n))$ as

$$(S_{pp}(n) = \frac{1}{T} \int_0^T \{[I_1^2(n) + I_2^2(n)]/2\} dt$$

so that

$$\sigma_p^2 = \int_0^\infty S_{pp}(n) dn.$$

The spectral density function shows how each frequency band contributes to the 'variance' (the square of the standard deviation), and ties together the definitions in the magnitude and frequency regimes.

If a value of the variance for an averaging time of t_a is required, it can be calculated from the last equation by changing the limits of the integration, thus

$$\sigma_p^2(t_a) = \int_0^{1/t_a} S_{pp}(n) dn.$$

The value of pressure which has a given probability of being exceeded can be calculated from this in the same way as before, providing the shape of the probability density function is the same as before.

In a wind tunnel investigation, in which a series of values of pressure is measured, the value which has a given 'probability of exceedence' can be evaluated directly. However, approximations to the shape of the probability density function for certain parameters have been postulated and are widely used. The most widely used is the 'Weibull distribution' for the occurrence of 'hourly-average wind speeds' in the atmosphere. This is usually quoted in the cumulative form:

$$P(V, WD) = p\{1 - \exp[-(V/c)^k]\},$$

where p is the probability that the wind is from direction WD, c is the 'mode' value and k is called the 'slope'.

These are all called 'parent distributions' because they are the distribution of a set of measurements which have actually been taken. However, sometimes in wind engineering, the largest value measured, or even one larger than any yet measured is required. This sounds an unlikely requirement but it is not because it is obvious that, if the original sample is of reasonable length, and had the sample been continued much further there could have been a larger value in it, provided that there is no physical reason for a maximum value which cannot be exceeded. This is the science of 'extreme value analysis'.

These techniques have been used extensively in the compilation of the Code, and a short introduction is presented here, a reader who requires further details is referred to a textbook on statistics.

If $P_1(x_0)$ is the probability that the value of x is less than x_0 in one sample, then, by the binomial distribution, the probability that the value of x is less than x_0 in N samples is $P_N(x_0)$ where

$$P_N(x_0) = [P_1(x_0)]^N.$$

Because the shape of the distribution can be shown not to be affected by a linear distribution, it follows that

$$P_N(x_0 + b(N)) = [P_1(x_0)]^N.$$

This equation is reduced, see Gumbel,[8] so that the distribution for the extreme value values (as N tends to ∞) becomes

$$P_1(x_0) = \exp\{-\exp[-\alpha(x_0 - U)]\},$$

where U and α are constants independent of N.

This is called by Gumbel[8] the 'first asymptote' and by Fisher and Tippet,[9] who first evaluated the expression, their 'Type 1' solution. There are two other solutions 'Type 2' and 'Type 3' in which there are an upper and a lower limit on the value of the variable x.

U is called the 'mode' of the distribution and $1/\alpha$ is called the 'dispersion'. The value $(U \times \alpha)$ is called the 'characteristic product'.

It has been found that the parent distribution for dynamic pressure reaches its asymptotic value much quicker than the wind speed, so that all recent work is based upon dynamic pressure. From measurements of dynamic pressure in the atmosphere the value of the characteristic product is found to be very close to 5 in all circumstances; consequently that value is accepted universally. Thus the distribution can be rewritten

$$\alpha x_0 = (U \times \alpha) - \ln\{-\ln[P_1(x_0)]\},$$

and the ratio of two values of x_o, x_1 and x_2 which have probabilities of exceedence in any one year (sample) of $P_1(x_1)$ and $P_1(x_2)$ is given by

$$\left\{5 - \ln[-\ln\{P_1(x_1)\}]\right\} / \left\{5 - \ln[-\ln\{P_1(x_2)\}]\right\},$$

and the square root of the expression when wind speeds are considered.

This is the expression given in Appendix F, noting that $P_1(x_0)$ is the cumulative probability that the variable x is *less* than x_0 in any one year (sample). A similar equation appears in Appendix D, where

$$\alpha(x - U) = y$$

and y is called the 'reduced variate' and values of peak dynamic pressure or wind speed are plotted against the natural log of the reduced variate.

---

[8] E.J. Gumbel, *Statistics of Extremes*, Columbia University Press, NY 1958.
[9] R.A. Fisher and L.H.C. Tippett, Limiting forms of the frequency distribution of the largest and smallest member of a sample, *Proc. Cantab. Philos. Soc.*, Vol **24**, 1928, pp. 160–90.